BASICS OF
ELECTRICITY

by

LEO A. MEYER

H. LYNN WRAY, P.E., Technical Advisor

INDOOR ENVIRONMENT
TECHNICIANS LIBRARY

**LAMA
BOOKS**

FOREWORD

You are probably working as a technician in one of the indoor environment fields. This means that you have at least some understanding of electricity. However, don't fall into the trap of thinking, "I know all this stuff."

Read each chapter. Then do the Review. In my experience, every time I studied material I "knew all about," I learned new ideas and corrected misunderstandings.

If you study each chapter carefully, you will gain new ideas. More important, you will give yourself a solid understanding of basic principles that you will be able to apply in the field. You will also be able to apply your knowledge to more advanced technical principles covered in later books in this series.

Indoor Environment Technician's Library

This book is part of the *Indoor Environment Technician's Library*. These are practical books that you can use as training or as reference. These books apply to all areas of the indoor environment industry:

> Heating, ventilating, and air conditioning
> Energy management
> Indoor air quality
> Service work
> Testing, adjusting, and balancing

If You Are Training Others

If you are a supervisor training others, you will find that the *Indoor Environment Technician's Library* can make it easier. A Supervisor's Guide is available for each book. It includes teaching suggestions and key questions you can ask to make sure the student understands the material.

Leo A. Meyer

LAMA Books
Leo A. Meyer Associates Inc.
23850 Clawiter Road
Hayward CA 94545-1723
510-785-1091

ISBN 0-88069-016-X

TABLE OF CONTENTS

1 ELECTRICAL SAFETY

When you complete this chapter, you will be able to:

- ☐ Recognize the dangers of electricity.

- ☐ Identify polarized plugs, grounded plugs, GFCI outlets, and 220V 3-prong plugs.

- ☐ Avoid making your body an electrical conductor.

- ☐ Turn power off and make sure it stays off.

- ☐ Avoid causing damage to equipment or conductors.

- ☐ Take emergency measures to rescue someone who has received a shock.

THE DANGERS OF ELECTRICITY

You use electricity every day of your life, so it is easy to take it for granted. **Yet electricity is a major cause of injury on the job.**

A jolt of electricity can hurt you, burn you, knock you unconscious, or kill you. How much electricity will kill you? It's hard to say. An amount that might just give you a slight shock one time might kill you another time. Damp skin, wet ground, metal-tipped shoes, or a two-handed grip can make even a relatively small amount of electricity fatal. Current as low as 5 milliamps can be dangerous in some cases.

The main danger of electricity is that the voltage clamps your heart muscle and causes a very irregular movement. As a result, your heart stops pumping, blood circulation stops, and you stop breathing. If CPR is started immediately, it may be able to revive someone who has stopped breathing because of an electric shock. Electric shock can also cause other muscle spasms. If someone touches a live electrical line, a muscle spasm of the hands may make it impossible to let go of the wire. High voltage can cause burns.

If you are on a ladder or a scaffold, a shock can cause you to fall.

Another danger is that electricity can start a fire. Electrical fires often start out of sight and can become dangerous before they are even noticed.

Electricity is safe only if you use all the safeguards built into the system, as well as common-sense safe working practices. Can you answer these questions?

- ☐ You turn off the power in order to work on a circuit. Yet you get a shock. Why?

- ☐ You turn off the power and remove the electrical connections to a motor before working on the motor. Yet you still get a shock. Why?

- ☐ Someone working on a 110 volt house circuit gets a shock and dies. Why?

- ☐ Your buddy on the job receives a 440 volt shock, is unconscious, and is still connected to the wires. What should you do?

This chapter will give you answers to these questions.

ELECTRICAL CIRCUITS

To work safely with electricity, you should know a few things about it. Think of electricity flowing in a wire circuit like water flowing in a pipe. Electricity is safe as long as it flows in the **circuit** designed for it.

In a proper circuit, electricity flows from the power source through a conductor to the energy-using device (motor, lamp, heater) and back to the power source

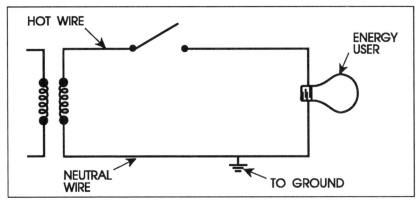

Fig. 1: A single-phase AC circuit has a hot wire and a neutral wire. The neutral wire is grounded

(Fig. 1). In a single-phase circuit, one wire connected to the switch for the energy-user is the **hot wire** (Fig. 1). The other wire is the **neutral wire** (Fig. 1). The neutral wire is always **grounded.** That is, it is attached to something that would conduct electricity to the ground where it would be neutralized. The neutral wire is sometimes mistakenly called the **ground wire** because it is grounded.

Some materials are good **conductors.** That is, they allow electricity to move through them easily. Silver, copper, aluminum, most other metals, and water are good conductors.

Some materials are good **insulators.** They offer high resistance and do not allow electricity to move easily through them. Rubber, glass, most plastics, and dry air are good insulators.

Other materials are in between—neither good conductors nor good insulators.

The difference between conductors and insulators makes it possible to use electricity safely by keeping it contained within a circuit. Copper is commonly used for wiring because it is a good conductor at a reasonable price. The wire is protected with insulation that keeps the electricity from escaping to anything else—such as people.

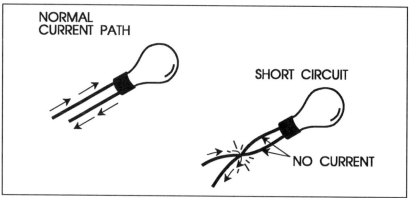

Fig. 2: A short circuit causes high current flow in the conductor

Short Circuits

Trouble starts when electricity escapes from the circuit designed for it. It might happen because the insulation is damaged, perhaps because excessive electric current causes high heat in the conductor and burns through the insulation. It might happen because damaged wires allow the electricity to bypass the energy-using device such as the lamp in Fig. 2. Since the bypass has less resistance than the path through the lamp, more current surges through the **short circuit.** The high current heats up the conductor and can burn through the insulation. This type of short circuit can cause a fire, explosion, or other damage to people or equipment.

Escaped electricity will find a path that leads to the ground where it is neutralized so that it is no longer dangerous. If you become part of that path, the electricity flows through you and into the ground (Fig. 3). You get a shock.

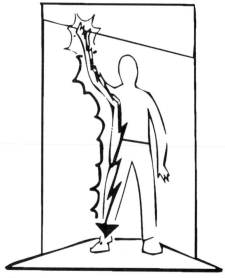

Fig. 3: You are a good path for electricity

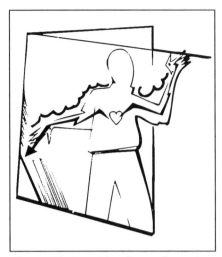

Fig. 4: If electricity flows through your heart, it may stop

Electricity always takes the path of least resistance. It flows through the best conductor. Unfortunately, the human body is a good conductor, since it is mostly water. If a human body is in contact with the ground, electricity can easily flow through the body to the ground. If it flows through your heart on its path to the ground, your heart may stop (Fig. 4). When you work with electricity, your basic safety practice is to keep from being a conductor to ground.

On DC circuits, you must touch both wires to be shocked. However, automotive DC circuits are grounded by being connected to the auto frame and engine. Touching the hot wire and the car frame is the same as touching both wires.

STORED ELECTRICITY

Electricity isn't always moving through wires. It can also be stored in various ways. A **battery** is a familiar way of storing electricity in a DC circuit. In AC motors and other electrical equipment, a **capacitor** is a small component that stores electricity. Even when the equipment is completely disconnected from any power source, a capacitor may hold enough electricity to give you a shock if you touch it. You have to know how to discharge the stored electricity in the capacitor by letting it escape to ground. This process is described in Chapter 7.

COMMON VOLTAGES

In general, the higher the voltage in a given circuit, the higher the current, and therefore the more dangerous the shock. Human skin usually resists anything under 48 volts, so you probably won't feel a voltage under this amount.

Most power used in homes and small businesses is 110 to 120 volts (V). However, almost every house has a 220 volt circuit for large appliances such as the washer and dryer. On the job, you may encounter 208V, 220V, 230V, 440V, or 460V. Anything over 600V is considered high voltage and requires special protection devices.

WALL PLUGS

The wall outlet and plugs for 110V or 120V can be one of five kinds:

- ☐ **Old style 2-prong plug.** It has no safety feature and it is obsolete. It is seldom seen except on inexpensive extension cords.

- ☐ **Polarized 2-prong plug** (Fig. 5). One flat prong is wider than the other. It can be plugged in only one way so that the neutral wire of the circuit is connected to the neutral wire of the equipment and the hot wire of the circuit to the hot wire of the equipment. There is less chance of a short and fewer electrical problems for the equipment. The polarized plug provides some protection from electrical shock, but not as much as the 3-prong grounded plug.

- ☐ **Grounded 3-prong plug** (Fig. 6). A round prong is grounded to the frame of the equipment. If there is a short, current will pass through the grounded plug—not through you. This ground wire is separate

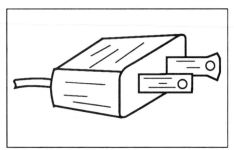

Fig. 5: A polarized plug has one prong wider than the other

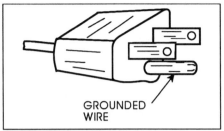

Fig. 6: A grounded plug has one round prong

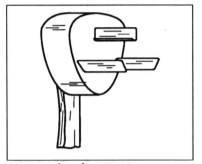

Fig. 8: Plug for 220V single-phase circuit

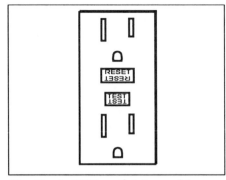

Fig. 7: A GFCI outlet is used in wet conditions

from the grounded neutral wire of the circuit. A 3-prong plug is usually used with rotating equipment such as a drill motor.

☐ **Ground-fault circuit interrupter (GFCI or GFI) (Fig. 7).** Electrical outlets exposed to the weather or to other wet conditions (such as bathrooms) must be GFCI outlets. The GFCI monitors the current in the two wires of the circuit. These two currents should be equal (within a certain tolerance). If they are not equal, there is a short and the GFCI disconnects the circuit. A GFCI outlet has a reset button on it.

☐ **220V plug (Fig. 8).** The wall outlet for a 220V circuit has a special design to accept a plug with three flat prongs (or some other special pattern) so that it cannot be confused with a 110 volt circuit.

AVOID ELECTRICAL DANGERS

There are four main kinds of danger from electricity:

☐ Shock (ranging from a mild jolt to death)

- ☐ Fire

- ☐ Burns (which may spread beyond the surface burn that shows)

- ☐ Injury (from machinery started up while you work on it; from a shock that causes you to fall into moving equipment or knocks you off a ladder or scaffold)

Fortunately, by following safety rules, you can avoid most electrical accidents.

PROTECT YOURSELF

Your first line of defense against electricity is to keep yourself from being a conductor.

- ☐ Keep dry. If at all possible, avoid working on electrical equipment if you are wet. Never work on an electrical system if your shoes are wet.

- ☐ Don't stand in puddles or on wet ground. If possible, stand on an approved rubber mat or wood platform when you work on electrical equipment (Fig. 9).

- ☐ Wear rubber-soled shoes (Fig. 9).

- ☐ Don't wear metal, such as a watch, ring, or other jewelry. These can cause accidents in three ways: They can catch in machinery, they can conduct electricity, they can cause a severe burn as electricity arcs between the body and the metal.

- ☐ Avoid contact with metal pipes because they provide a perfect ground.

- ☐ Use a wood ladder, not a metal ladder.

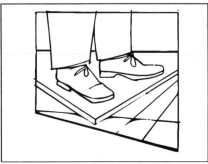

Fig. 9: Stand on a dry board or rubber mat. Wear rubber-soled shoes

Fig. 10: Use one hand only when you work around live circuits

☐ If you must work around energized circuits, use one hand only (Fig. 10). If both hands are in contact, the electrical path can go from one arm across the heart to the other arm (Fig. 4). If only one hand is in contact, the shock goes from the arm down a leg to the ground (Fig. 3).

KEEP IT TURNED OFF

Never **assume** that a circuit is turned off. Of course you will turn off the power to any equipment you have to service, but you must make sure it really is off and that it stays off. Too many accidents have happened because one worker turned a switch on after another worker had turned it off for good reason. There are two dangers:

☐ Electricity can cause a shock.

☐ Equipment started when you aren't expecting it can injure or kill.

If you want it off, **make sure it stays off.**

For equipment on an electric cord, unplug it before you work on it, and put a warning tag on the plug telling others that you are working on the equipment.

Fig. 11: Lock it out and tag it

For equipment with permanent electrical connections, turn off the power source. Lock it out with your own padlock. Even if a switch is already locked out, put your own padlock on it. Tag the lock with your name, location, and date (Fig. 11).

Even if you have turned off the main power or disconnect, take a voltage reading on the lines to be sure they are dead (Fig. 12). If the switch is not properly wired, there could be power in the circuit even though the switch is in the off position.

Make sure that any capacitor is discharged safely before you begin work. If you do not know how to do this, get someone to show you. The process is explained in Chapter 7.

Fig. 12: Take a voltage reading to make sure the circuit is dead

Remove locks and tags as soon as you are done working. If they are left on longer than needed, other workers won't take them seriously in the future. Make sure you have your own lock and tags.

KEEP EQUIPMENT SAFE

Don't use faulty equipment. If anything electrical—from a small hand tool to a major piece of equipment—is damaged in some way it is not safe. Get it checked or replaced.

☐ Replace frayed or damaged electrical cords.

☐ Don't let cords get twisted, kinked, or crushed. Protect them from heat, chemicals, and oil. Protect extension cords on the floor with a cover designed for the purpose or use a board on each side of the cord (Fig. 13).

☐ Disconnect cords by pulling on the plug, not the cord.

☐ Don't overload a conductor. For power tools, use a heavy-duty extension cord that is rated for the load. A light duty cord will over-heat and may destroy the cord or cause a voltage drop that can harm equipment.

☐ Don't use a power tool if the grounding prong has been removed.

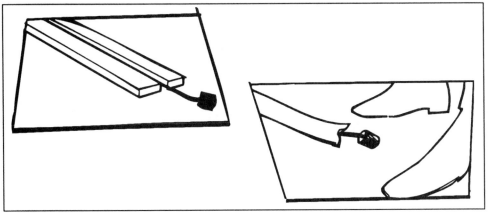

Fig. 13: Protect electrical cords on the floor

☐ If using a piece of equipment causes the power to go off, find out why. The tool may be defective and dangerous.

☐ If motor windings are dirty, have proper maintenance done.

☐ If equipment smokes, sparks, or gives a shock, **don't use it.**

☐ If a tool does not work consistently, get it repaired.

☐ Keep tools and equipment dry.

☐ Don't overload a circuit or piece of equipment.

USE SAFETY FEATURES

Don't try to get around safety features. Safety features are there for a reason.

☐ If covers on switch boxes or other equipment must be removed, replace them as soon as possible. Exposed electrical contacts could cause electrical shock.

12

- If equipment has a safety switch that turns off automatically, use the reset button only once. If the safety switch turns off a second time, the equipment should be checked and repaired.

Fig. 14: Use an adapter properly attached

- Use a 3-prong grounded plug in a 3-hole outlet. Never cut off the third prong. If no 3-hole outlet is available, buy an adapter and connect it to the metal screw of the cover plate (Fig. 14).

- Never file or cut the wide prong of a polarized plug to fit it into an old outlet.

- Don't bypass fuses or circuit breakers or replace them with larger ones.

- Don't use an outlet if it may become damp unless it is a GFCI (ground-fault circuit interrupter). This is an outlet that breaks the circuit if moisture or anything else causes a short circuit.

SAFETY TIPS

- Wiring may not have been installed according to code. Don't depend on it. Don't assume by color that a wire is the neutral wire. It may be hot.

Shark from 'Jaws' claims new victim

HOLLYWOOD (UPI) — The mechanical shark that terrified theater-goers in the movie "Jaws" and now leaps from a lagoon and snaps at tourists visiting Universal Studios sent a workman to the hospital today.

Barry Alkira, 30, a painter at the studio, was working on the fin of the life-like shark when the mock sea creature was "inadvertently activated," a Universal spokesman said.

Alkira was apparently thrown through the air and dragged by the "shark." He was taken by ambulance to St. Joseph's Medical Center in Burbank with possible back injuries.

Newspaper clipping

- Remove and replace motor starter covers carefully so that they don't touch a live contact in the box or pinch the insulation.

- If wires must be pulled out of a live box for reading amperage, pull them out carefully with your fingers. If you use a screwdriver to pull them out, you might cut through the insulation and touch the bare wire.

- Unless absolutely necessary, do not try to override interlocks that turn off the power when an electrical cabinet cover is removed. Sometimes it is necessary to do this when measuring amperage. If so, be sure you know the manufacturer's recommended method of overriding the interlock, or ask an experienced technician how to do it.

- Don't store rubbish or rags near electrical equipment.

- Know where fire extinguishers are located. Find out if they can be used on electrical fires. Don't use water on an electrical fire.

WHAT TO DO IN CASE OF ELECTRICAL SHOCK

Every emergency is different. The general advice that follows may not fit every situation exactly. You must use your good judgment when you help someone who received an electric shock.

Don't become a victim yourself. Live electric current can flow from one body to another. Don't touch someone who is still in contact with electricity.

If the victim is in contact with current, **cut off the contact:**

- ☐ Throw the switch for that circuit if you can.

- ☐ Use a piece of dry wood to move the wire from the victim.

- ☐ If necessary cut the electrical cable to the victim using a tool with a wooden or plastic handle. Protect your eyes from the flash when the wires are cut.

- ☐ Drag or pull the victim away by using a **nonconductor,** such as a dry board, rope, blanket, coat, or belt.

Once the victim is free of the current, check for pulse, heart beat, breathing, or an obstruction in the throat. If the victim is not breathing, use CPR if you are trained. Get help by calling 911 (or your local emergency number) or by having someone else call.

Loosen the victim's clothing to allow free breathing. Keep the victim lying down or resting. The heart may be very weak, and sudden activity could cause heart failure. Do not give the victim alcohol or medications. Keep the victim from getting too hot or too cold. **Don't leave the victim until medical help arrives.** There could be a relapse.

Your first responsibility is to keep from making yourself or someone else a victim of electricity. Keep a healthy fear of electricity and never just assume that conditions are safe. You may not have a second chance to guess right.

Worker Dies

A worker was fatally injured at a local rolling mill last night. The victim was doing maintenance work on machinery. When power to the machine was turned on, a large metal gate dropped, broke its safety chains, and fell on the victim, crushing his head.

Newspaper clipping

Worker Hit by Electrical Wire

A worker was treated for electrical shock at the hospital after an on-the-job accident. According to the deputy sheriff, the worker was installing drywall when he backed up and an electrical wire hanging from the ceiling hit him on the side of the head.

Newspaper clipping

REVIEW

If you can answer the following questions without referring to the text, you have learned the contents of this chapter. Try to answer every question **before** you check the answers in the back of the book.

1. Name at least 3 conditions that could make a jolt of electricity more dangerous to you.

2. In a single-phase circuit, what are the 2 wires connected to a circuit?

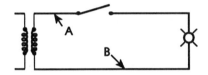

3. Of the following materials, which are good insulators? Which are good conductors?

Water
Dry air
Glass
Silver
Rubber

Aluminum
Plastic
Copper
Human body

4. Why is a short circuit dangerous?

5. Name 2 devices for storing electricity.

6. What is a GFCI and what does it do?

7. How can you make sure that equipment on an electric cord stays safe to work on while you service it?

8. How can you make sure that equipment with permanent electrical connections stays safe to work on while you service it?

9. What are 2 dangers of using a light-duty extension cord for power tools?

10. What is your local emergency number?

11. Your buddy on a construction job has been knocked unconscious by an electrical shock and is still in contact with the live conductor. What are possible actions you could take immediately?

Give **one** possible answer to each of the following:

12. You turn off the power before working on a piece of equipment but get a shock anyway. Why?

13. You turn off the power to a piece of equipment and remove the electrical connections, but while you are working you suddenly get a shock. Why?

14. Dan once received a shock on a 110 volt circuit and was not seriously harmed, so he was relaxed about working with electricity. While working on another 110 volt circuit, he had a similar accident, received a shock, and died. Why?

Check your answers in the back of the book.

2

BASIC ELECTRICITY IN DC CIRCUITS

When you complete this chapter, you will be able to:

☐ Explain the terms volts, amps, ohms, watts, conductor, insulator, current, and circuit.

☐ Explain how volts, amps, and ohms are related according to Ohm's Law.

☐ Identify different types of circuits.

WORKING WITH ELECTRICITY

Working with electricity is dangerous. However, the more you understand it, the safer you will be around it. You have to know how to work safely with electricity if you work with an indoor environment system.

ELECTRICAL FLOW

The most common theory to explain electrical flow is the **electron theory.** An atom has a center called a **nucleus** which is a cluster of particles that have a positive charge. Particles called **electrons,** which have a negative charge, orbit around the nucleus in different rings (Fig. 1). Electrical flow occurs when

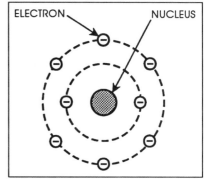

Fig. 1: An atom

electrons move from the ring of one atom to the ring of another.

Some materials have electrons that move easily from one atom to another. These materials are good **conductors.** Copper, which is used in wiring, is the most common conductor. However, other materials, especially metals, also conduct electricity well. Certain gases that conduct electricity are used in fluorescent and neon lamps. Water is a very good conductor of electricity.

Some materials have atoms that do not give up electrons easily. These are good **insulators.** Insulators are used to cover conductors, such as copper wiring, to avoid short circuits and shock. As you have already learned, glass, ceramic, plastics, rubber, and other materials are good insulators.

For electricity to be useful, it has to follow a definite path. Electricity flows from an **energy source** (a battery or generator), through a **conductor** (wire), to an **energy-using device** (motor, lamp, heater, etc.), then back to the **energy source** (Fig. 2). The complete path is called an electrical **circuit.**

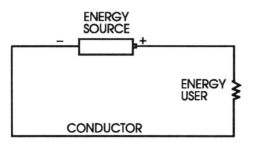

Fig. 2: An electric circuit provides a complete path so that electricity continues to flow

TYPES OF ELECTRICAL CURRENT

There are two common types of electrical systems—direct current (DC) and alternating current (AC).

Direct current (DC) means that the electrical current flows in one direction. Batteries deliver DC current. Most electronic devices and most automobile circuits are DC.

Alternating current (AC) means that the current flows first in one direction and then in the other. Alternating current will be discussed in Chapter 5.

This chapter uses direct current circuits to explain electrical basics. A DC circuit is easier to understand than an AC circuit. However, the basic principles of DC circuits also apply to AC circuits.

THE DC CIRCUIT

An electrical circuit carries the flow of electricity from one component of the electrical system to another. Compare the electricity flowing in an electrical circuit to the water flowing in a piping system. Both an electrical circuit and a piping system have the following components:

☐ Pressure source

☐ Conductor

☐ Control device

☐ Energy-user

First consider how these four work in a piping system (Fig. 3):

☐ The **pressure source** is the pump that moves the water.

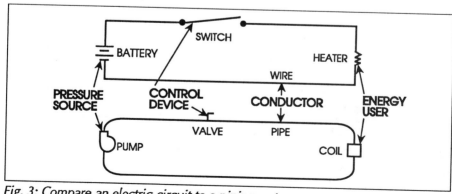

Fig. 3: Compare an electric circuit to a piping system

- ☐ The **conductor** is the pipe that transports the water through the system.

- ☐ The **control device** is the valve that turns the flow of the water on or off.

- ☐ The **energy-user** is the coil which removes heat energy from the water in the pipe.

The four components work in a similar way in a DC circuit (Fig. 3):

- ☐ The **pressure source** is the battery.

- ☐ The **conductor** is the wire.

- ☐ The **control device** is the switch.

- ☐ The **energy-user** is the heater, lamp, or other load.

Pressure Source

In Fig. 4, the pressure source is a battery. It stores a charge of electricity to be used when needed. Batteries have a positive terminal and a negative terminal. The DC current flows in one direction from one terminal to the other.

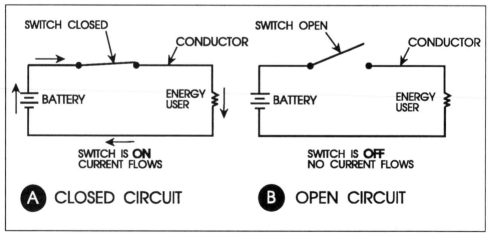

Fig. 4: A closed circuit has current flowing

Conductor

The **conductor** in Fig. 4 is the circuit wiring.

Control Device

The **control device** (Fig. 4) is the switch that controls the flow of electricity:

☐ If the switch is *on*, the circuit is closed (Fig. 4A) and electrical current can complete its path.

☐ If the switch is *off*, the circuit is open (Fig. 4B) because there is a break in the path for the electrical current.

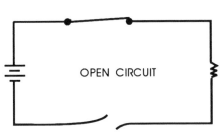

Fig. 5: Circuit is open if the conductor is broken

A circuit is also open if a wire or connection is broken so that the electrical flow cannot complete the circuit (Fig. 5). In a case like this, the circuit is open even though the switch is closed.

Many different switches are used in the indoor environment system. Some operate manually, others operate automatically.

Energy-User

The **energy-user** (called the **load**) in a circuit is any equipment that uses the energy of the electrical current. Electric heaters or lamps are **resistive** energy users. They have a conductor material (such as a light bulb filament) that has a high resistance to the flow of electricity. Electricity has to push its way through the resistance, and the energy given off causes the conductor to heat up or glow. A circuit that has only resistive energy users is called a **resistive circuit**.

Circuit Protection

To prevent damage from a short circuit, some kind of circuit protection is needed.

Fuses in a DC circuit (Fig. 6) are designed to melt and break a circuit before the temperature gets high enough to do damage.

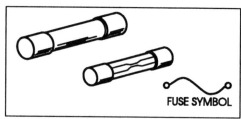

FUSE SYMBOL

Fig. 6: Fuses

SCHEMATICS

If you work with electrical systems, you have to learn to read wiring diagrams called **schematics**. Schematics use symbols and abbreviations to simplify a wiring system. You have already used some very simple schematics in Figs. 2, 3, 4, and 5.

Figure 7 shows some of the common symbols used for DC wiring schematics. Often a schematic may have a key to the symbols and abbreviations used. However, if you use schematics, you soon learn to recognize most symbols without looking them up.

Building plans show where each electrical device is located. The schematic diagram does not show locations but shows how the wiring is to be run and how the electrical devices are related. Figure 8 shows a simple DC schematic. Another book in this series teaches you how to read complex schematics.

VOLTS, AMPS, AND OHMS

An electrical circuit in a DC system has three components (Fig. 9):

☐ **Voltage** (electrical pressure)—Created by a battery or generator. Also called *potential.*

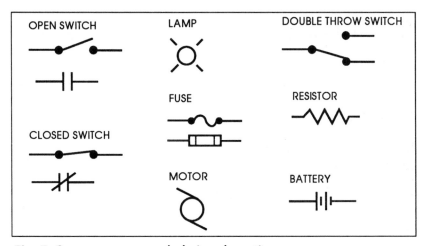

Fig. 7: Some common symbols in schematics

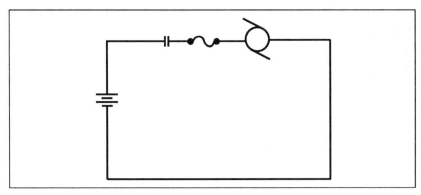

Fig. 8: A simple DC schematic

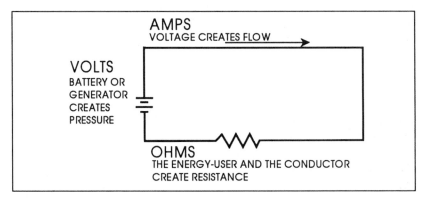

Fig. 9: Volts, amps, and ohms

❏ **Amperage** (current flow)—The rate at which the electrical current flows in the conductor.

❏ **Ohms** (resistance to flow)—A measure of the resistance to the flow of electricity in the conductor or the energy user.

This book uses the abbreviations V (voltage), A (amperage), and O (ohms). Other texts may use the following traditional symbols:

❏ E (voltage)

❏ I (amperage)

❏ R or Ω (ohms)

Voltage

To move water in a piping system, a pressure source such as a pump creates a pressure to start the water moving. An electrical circuit also needs a pressure source such as a battery or generator. The force produced is called **voltage** or **potential.** Electricity, like air in a duct or water in a pipe, flows from the higher pressure to the lower.

Amperage

In a piping system, the rate of flow is measured in gallons per minute. Amperage, the rate at which electricity flows in a circuit, is measured in **amperes,** commonly called **amps.** In general, if the pressure (voltage) increases, then the rate of flow (amperage) also increases.

Ohms

The flow of water in a piping system has some resistance from the friction with the walls of the pipe and much more resistance from a heating or cooling coil. In an electrical circuit, the flow of electricity meets some resistance from the wiring and much more resistance from any energy-user, such as a lamp. The resistance in a circuit is measured in **ohms.**

A small gage wire creates more resistance than a larger gage wire. When the cross-sectional area of a conductor is doubled, its resistance is cut in half. A higher current needs larger conductors than a smaller current so that there will not be too much resistance.

OHM'S LAW

OHM'S LAW

VOLTS = AMPS X OHMS

Fig. 10: Ohm's Law shows how volts, amps, and ohms are related

The volts, amps, and ohms in a circuit are all related. If the amount of one of these forces is changed, another amount will also change.

Ohm's Law (Fig. 10) is a simple equation that shows how the volts, amps, and ohms in a circuit are related:

Volts = Amps x Ohms

This equation can be used in two other forms in order to find amps and ohms:

$$Amps = \frac{Volts}{Ohms}$$

$$Ohms = \frac{Volts}{Amps}$$

Ohm's Law can be used to see what happens in a circuit when one value changes. For example, if a circuit has a 10 volt battery and operates a lamp with a resistance of 3 ohms, then the flow of electricity in the circuit must be 4 amps:

$$Amps = \frac{12\ volts}{3\ ohms}$$

Amps = 4

If another lamp is added to the circuit in series so that the resistance is increased to 6 ohms, what is the amperage?

$$Amps = \frac{12\ volts}{6\ ohms}$$

Amps = 2

The increased resistance means that the current has decreased to 2 amps.

The AC circuits you will work on normally have fixed voltage, such as 110V or 220V building wiring and 24V automatic control circuits. The two values that vary are amps and ohms. If one increases, the other decreases (Fig. 11):

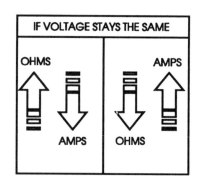

☐ If resistance is increased, amperage decreases.

☐ If resistance is decreased, amperage increases.

Fig. 11: If ohms are increased, amps decrease. If ohms are decreased, amps increase.

In other words, the rate of flow lowers when resistance is increased.

Consider the following DC circuit that requires 30 amps to power a resistance load:

120 volts = 30 amps x 4 ohms

Suppose smaller wiring is installed or the length of the wiring is increased so that the resistance rises to 6 ohms. What is the amperage?

$$\text{Amps} = \frac{120 \text{ volts}}{6 \text{ oms}}$$

Amps = 20

The 20 amps in the circuit may not be enough to adequately operate the equipment.

On the job you will probably never use Ohm's Law to calculate values in a circuit. However, if you understand it, you can understand what will happen when something in a circuit changes.

This Ohm's Law equation applies only to DC circuits and AC resistive circuits (circuits that use resistance to provide light or heat). Reactive circuits (circuits with electric motors) use magnetism, and magnetism affects the amperage. A more complex version of Ohm's Law is used for reactive circuits. However, the general relationship between volts, amps, and ohms remains the same.

REVIEW

If you can answer the following questions without referring to the text, you have learned the contents of this chapter. Try to answer every question **before** you check the answers in the back of the book.

1. If the amperage in a 120V resistive circuit is 25 amps, how many ohms resistance is there in the circuit?

2. After components in the circuit in question 1 are changed, the current is measured to be 30 amps. Has the number of ohms in the circuit increased or decreased?

3. A 12V circuit has a heater with a resistance of 5 ohms. There is little resistance in the conductor. What is the current in the circuit?

4. If another 5 ohm heater is added to the circuit in series, what is the amperage?

5. What do the terms *AC* and *DC* stand for?

6. Is the DC circuit for a lamp a *reactive circuit* or a *resistive circuit?*

7. Is the AC circuit for a drill motor a *reactive circuit* or a *resistive circuit?*

8. Is the AC circuit for an area heater a *reactive circuit* or a *resistive circuit?*

9. Name a device that provides short circuit protection in a DC circuit.

10. Identify each of the following as *voltage, amperage,* or *ohms:*

    A. Electrical pressure

    B. Resistance to electrical flow

    C. Electricity created by a generator

    D. Rate of current flow

    E. Battery output

    F. Caused by an energy user

    G. I

    H. Ω

    I. E

    J. R

11. The current in a circuit must be increased a great deal and the electrical wiring has to be changed. Should the wiring be changed to a larger or smaller size?

12. Write 3 versions of Ohm's Law.

13. Does the simple version of Ohm's Law apply to resistive circuits or to reactive circuits?

14. Identify the following symbols used on schematic diagrams:

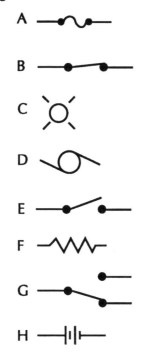

A

B

C

D

E

F

G

H

3

MAGNETISM AND ELECTRICITY

When you complete this chapter, you will be able to:

☐ Explain how magnets induce electric current, and how electricity creates a magnetic field.

MAGNETISM

Magnetism is what makes generators and electric motors work. It is also the reason transformers, solenoid valves, and automatic switches work. You cannot understand electrical devices until you understand how electricity and magnetism are related.

☐ Magnetism is used to generate an electric current.

☐ Electricity is used to generate magnetism.

Every molecule has a very small magnetic field with a north and a south pole. **Magnets** are metals that have their molecules lined up in the same direction. When the molecules are all lined up, their magnetic fields work together to create a larger, common magnetic field. When molecules do not line up in the same direction, their weak, individual magnetic fields are canceled out by the magnetic fields of molecules facing in other directions.

Iron, nickel, and cobalt are natural magnetic metals. They can be made into magnets by stroking them with another magnet. Some other metals can also become magnetic.

☐ **Soft iron** can be magnetized by an electric current. It loses its magnetism when the magnetic source is removed.

☐ **Steel** can be magnetized, and it will remain magnetic permanently.

The magnet used to magnetize another metal does not lose any of its magnetism in the process. Some metals (like copper and aluminum) cannot be magnetized.

Magnetic Field

Like the Earth, magnets always have two opposite poles—a north pole (N) and a south pole (S). Invisible **lines of force** that radiate from the magnetic poles are called the **magnetic field** (Fig. 1).

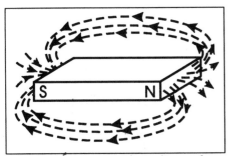

Fig. 1: A magnet with its lines of force

To see the lines of force, sprinkle iron filings on a piece of cardboard and hold a magnet under the cardboard. Gently tap the cardboard and the filings will arrange themselves according to the magnetic lines of force.

Law of Magnetism

You can feel magnets pushing each other apart when you try to touch two like poles together. You can also feel the attraction between unlike poles (north to south) of two magnets. The basic law of magnetism has two parts:

☐ **Like poles repel each other** (Fig. 2).

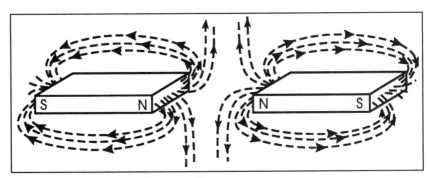

Fig. 2: Like poles repel each other

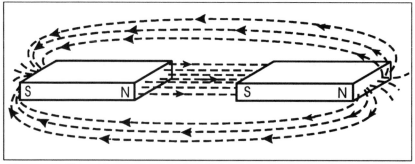

Fig. 3: Unlike poles attract each other

☐ **Unlike poles attract each other** (Fig. 3).

Flux Density

The magnetic lines of force are also called the **flux**. The strength of a magnetic field is called its **flux density**. The stronger the magnetic field, the greater the flux density, and the greater number of lines of force. Flux density increases when opposite poles of two magnets are moved closer.

CREATING ELECTRICAL CURRENT

Magnetic force can be used to create electrical voltage. If you pass a conductor through a magnetic field, electrical voltage is created, or **induced**, in the conductor. This is the basic principle of electric generators.

Induction generates electric voltage (and resulting flow of current) by using a magnetic field. Generators, electric motors, and transformers are all based on induction.

The amount of voltage generated by induction is related to the flux density of the magnetic field. A greater flux density creates greater voltage in the conductor.

Creating Alternating Current

The direction of current flow in the conductor is determined by the north/south polarity of the magnetic field, and by the direction the wire conductor is moved through the field.

- ☐ If a wire conductor is moved from left to right through the field shown in Fig. 4, current will flow from A to B.

- ☐ If the wire is moved in the opposite direction through the field, current will flow from B to A (Fig. 5).

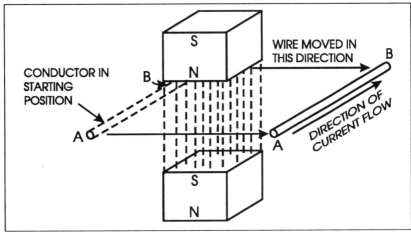

Fig. 4: If the wire moves from left to right, current flows from A to B

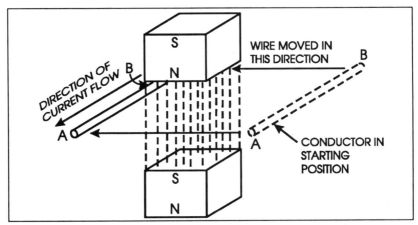

Fig. 5: If the wire moves from right to left, current flows from B to A

This change of direction is used to create **alternating current (AC)**. This is done by rotating a wire loop (called an **armature**) through a magnetic field.

The loop in Fig. 6 is rotating clockwise. Since the part of the loop labeled A-B is passing through the field from **left to right**, current flows from A to B. At the same time, the part labeled C-D is passing through the field from **right to left**, making current flow from C to D. The part of the loop labeled B-C is not passing through the magnetic field. This part of the loop simply conducts electricity from B to C.

Current flows through the loop from X to A to B to C to D to Y, making the overall flow through the loop from X to Y (Fig. 6).

When the loop reaches the point shown in Fig. 7, no part of the loop is passing through the magnetic field. There is **no** current flow.

As the wire loop continues its rotation (Fig. 8), part A-B now passes through the field from right to left. Current flow is now from B to A, and from D to C. Overall flow during this part of the loop's rotation is reversed and is now from Y to X.

If the armature (the loop) keeps rotating through the magnetic field, the current flow keeps alternating

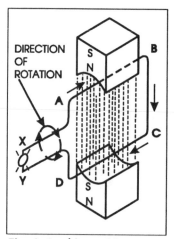

Fig. 6: In this position, current flows from X to Y

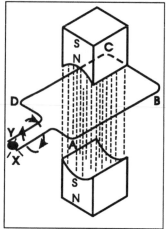

Fig. 7: No current flow

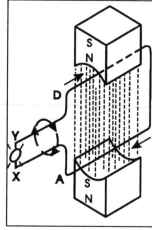

Fig. 8: In this position, current flows from Y to X

direction. This creates **alternating current (AC).** A complete rotation of the wire loop so that the current flows first in one direction and then in the other is called a **cycle.**

Sine Wave

The AC cycle is shown in a **sine wave** diagram (Fig. 9). As the loop rotates, the voltage sine wave begins rising from no voltage (zero) until it reaches the peak at the top of the wave, then decreases back to zero at 180°. When the voltage sine wave moves below the zero line, it means the current is flowing in the opposite direction because the voltage is reversed. After peaking in that direction, the sine wave moves back to zero at the end of the cycle. One AC cycle has been completed.

Each rotation of the loop is another cycle. Most utility companies in the United States supply alternating current at 60 cycles per second.

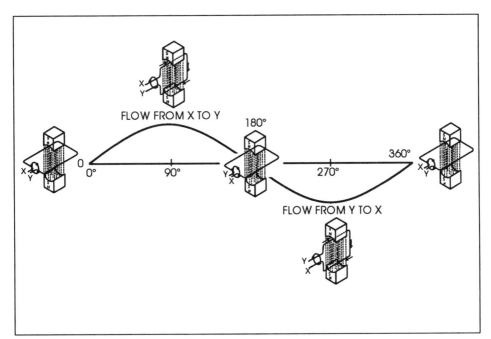

Fig. 9: Sine wave for one cycle of AC current

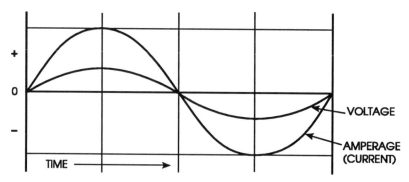

Fig. 10: Both voltage and amperage have a sine wave

The process that makes voltage alternate also causes amperage (current) to alternate. The alternating voltage and amperage are shown in a sine wave for a circuit with a resistive load (Fig. 10).

ELECTROMAGNETS

Just as a magnetic field can create an electric current, electricity can create a magnetic field:

☐ When electric current flows through a conductor, a magnetic field is created around the conductor (Fig. 11).

☐ As current flow increases, the magnetic lines of force increase.

☐ If the wire is looped in a **coil**, the magnetic field increases even more.

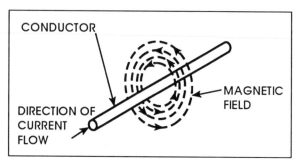

Fig. 11: Current creates a magnetic field

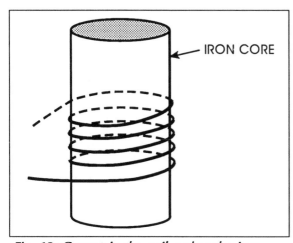

IRON CORE

Fig. 12: Current in the coil makes the iron core an electromagnet

□ If a core of soft iron is added to the coil of wire, the core becomes magnetized.

A soft iron core with many turns of conductor wire around it becomes an **electromagnet** (Fig. 12).

Soft iron is magnetized only as long as it is exposed to a magnetic field. When current is on, it becomes a magnet, but when current is off, it loses its magnetism. This is a very useful feature. Because magnetism can be turned on and off, it can do useful work.

Using Electricity and Magnetism

A **generator** converts mechanical energy into electrical energy. The mechanical energy can be provided by falling water, steam pressure, a fuel-powered engine, or even muscle power. Mechanical energy turns the wire loop that moves through a magnetic field so that the loop becomes electrified.

An **alternator** is a generator that produces alternating current. As you have learned, AC is produced by rotating a loop of wire through a magnetic field.

An **electric motor** converts electrical energy into mechanical energy. The push-pull effect of magnetism is used to drive a rotor which turns an attached shaft. The rotating shaft can drive a variety of machines mechanically.

Electromagnets are used in devices for hoisting or clamping, because the electric current that creates the magnetic force can be switched on or off.

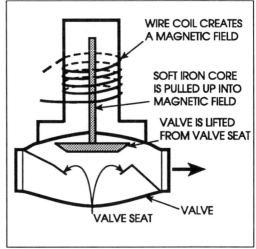

Fig. 13: Electromagnet used as a valve

The **push** or **pull** effect of magnetism is used in devices like solenoids that open or close valves. When the wire coil in Fig. 13 is energized, it becomes a magnet, so the plunger is pulled up, opening the valve.

REVIEW

If you can answer the following questions without referring to the text, you have learned the contents of this chapter. Try to answer every question **before** you check the answers in the back of the book.

1. Name three electrical devices that depend on magnetism for their operation.

2. Name three metals that make good magnets.

3. Name a metal that cannot be magnetized.

4. What is the term for creating an electric current by using a magnetic field?

5. What is a soft iron core with many turns of conductor wire wrapped around it?

Next to each drawing, write **repel** or **attract** to indicate the action of the magnets.

6.

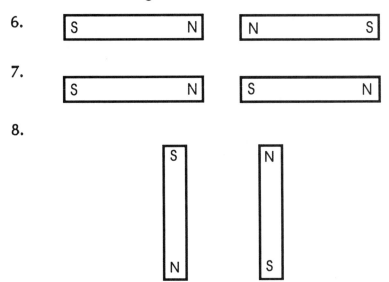

7.

8.

9. In the drawing below, is voltage being generated?

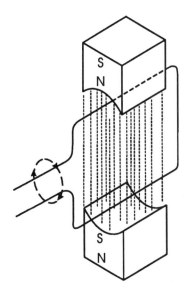

10. In the blank, write the letter from the drawing to match the description of the voltage.

_____Maximum positive voltage

_____Zero from negative phase

_____Zero from positive phase

_____Maximum negative voltage

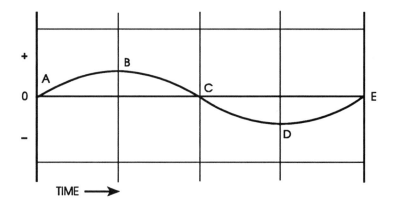

SERIES AND PARALLEL CIRCUITS

4

When you complete this chapter, you will be able to:

☐ Identify a series circuit and a parallel circuit.

☐ Sketch a simple series and a simple parallel circuit.

SERIES AND PARALLEL CIRCUITS

As you learned in Chapter 2, in order for electrical current to flow, there must be a conductor for it to travel through. A closed loop or continuous path in which electrical current flows is called an **electrical circuit.**

Two basic types of circuits are **series** and **parallel** circuits. You will encounter both when working with indoor environment systems. Knowing the principles of both types will help you understand how a device works.

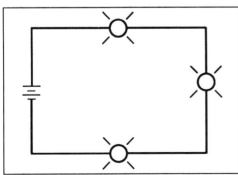

Fig. 1: Series circuit

SERIES CIRCUIT

In a series circuit, the energy-using devices (loads) are wired in series. That is, they are arranged so that the electric current flows in line from one device to the next (Fig. 1).

In a series circuit, the path of the current flows in a single line through each energy-using device. If there is a break at any point in the circuit, it will interrupt current flow to the whole circuit (Fig. 2).

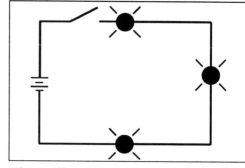

Fig. 2: Circuit open, no current flowing

Imagine a string of Christmas tree lights on a series circuit as in Fig. 1. If one light burns out, all of the lights on the string go out because the electrical circuit is no longer complete.

Series Resistance

Resistance of the energy-using devices in a series circuit, measured in ohms, is found by adding together the resistance of each device. Assume that each of the three lamps in Fig. 1 has a resistance of 3 ohms. The total resistance of the circuit is 9 ohms. (For simplification, the resistance of the conductor wire is not accounted for.)

Series Power

To meet power demands, energy **sources** can be wired in series, just as energy-using devices are wired in series. The effect of this is that the voltage produced by each power source is added together to produce the total voltage for that circuit. For example, if two 1½ volt batteries are connected in series (Fig. 3), 3 volts are produced. In a flashlight (Fig. 4), batteries are always connected end-to-end in a series. This is why a four-cell battery has more power than a two-cell battery. Two 1½ volt batteries produce 3 volts. Four 1½ volt batteries produce 6 volts.

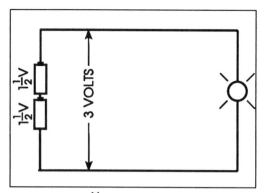

Fig. 3: Two 1½ volt batteries connected
in series—3 volts

Voltage Drop

Water in a pipe or air in a duct will not flow unless there is a pressure difference between the two ends of the circuit. In a domestic water system, the supply line provides about 40 psi (pounds per square inch). However, the water does not flow until a faucet is opened. psi. It is this pressure difference between 40 and 0 psi that makes the water flow. The same principle applies to an electrical circuit. There must be a pressure difference in the voltage of the circuit for the current (amperage) to flow.

In a series circuit, the resistance of each load (a lamp, for instance) creates a voltage drop. The total voltage drop of the circuit is equal to the voltage of the circuit. This is true whether there is one resistance load in the circuit or several.

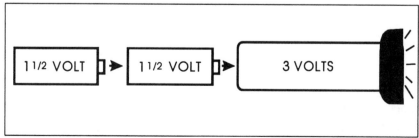

Fig. 4: Series power

PARALLEL CIRCUITS

Parallel circuits have as many current paths as there are energy-using devices (Fig. 5). There can be one or more branches where current flow divides to follow different conductor branches. This way, if the branch for one device opens, current can still flow to the remaining devices. The light circuits in a house

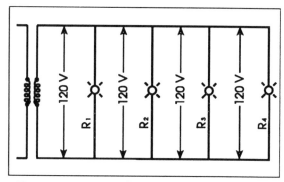

Fig. 5: Lamps wired in parallel

are parallel circuits. If one light is switched off or burns out, the rest of the lights in the circuit still work.

In a parallel circuit, each device has its own current path (or branch) called **branch current**. To calculate the branch current in a parallel circuit, you calculate for one branch at a time.

For example, if the parallel circuit in Fig. 5 has a power source of 120 volts, and the resistance of each lamp is 20 ohms, then the current through each branch is:

$$\text{Amps} = \frac{\text{Volts}}{\text{Ohms}}$$

$$\text{Amps} = \frac{120}{20}$$

Amps = 6 (for each branch)

Parallel Resistance

In **series** circuits, resistance increases with each new load added in the series, and total resistance is found by adding together the resistance of each load in the circuit. For **parallel** circuits, resistance decreases with

Please mark the following corrections in your book:

Page 45

In Fig. 5, assume that the lamps have the following
resistances:

$R_1 = 20$ ohms

$R_2 = 25$ ohms

$R_3 = 30$ ohms

$R_4 = 35$ ohms

Page 97

5. Inductive reactance and capacitive reactance

6. A capacitor stores voltage and releases it to resist
    changes in voltage.

7. Resistance, inductive reactance, capacitive reactance

8. No

9. Desirable to counteract inductive reactance

each new load in the circuit, and the total resistance is smaller than the resistance of any one of the loads.

The reason for this is that the current in a parallel circuit flows through more than one path. In Fig. 5, the current can flow through four different paths. Because of this, the total resistance in a parallel circuit is always less than that of any one of the resistors in the circuit.

The equation for finding the total resistance of this parallel circuit is:

$$R = \frac{1}{\left(\dfrac{1}{R_1}\right) + \left(\dfrac{1}{R_2}\right) + \left(\dfrac{1}{R_3}\right) + \left(\dfrac{1}{R_4}\right)}$$

R = Total resistance in the circuit

R_1 through R_4 = Resistance of each resistor in circuit

In Fig. 5, assume that the lamps have the following resistances:

R_1 = 20 ohms

R_2 = 20 ohms

R_3 = 20 ohms

R_4 = 20 ohms

The calculation for the total resistance of the circuit is:

$$R = \frac{1}{\left(\dfrac{1}{20}\right) + \left(\dfrac{1}{25}\right) + \left(\dfrac{1}{30}\right) + \left(\dfrac{1}{35}\right)}$$

$$R = \frac{1}{0.05 + 0.04 + 0.0333 + 0.0286}$$

$$R = \frac{1}{0.1519}$$

R = 6.583 (6.6 ohms)

Note that the circuit resistance (6.6 ohms) is much less than the resistance of any one load (20, 25, 30, and 35 ohms).

PARALLEL POWER

The power (voltage) for a circuit may also be connected in parallel (Fig. 6). Each power source supplies part of the current, and the current through each power source is considered **branch current**.

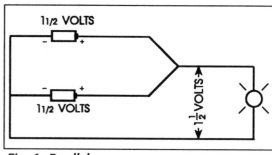

Fig. 6: Parallel power

It is possible to improperly wire parallel power. If wired incorrectly, the power sources may turn into a complete circuit, allowing no current to flow to the load (Fig. 7). In Fig. 7A one battery has been reversed. This makes a complete circuit through the batteries. No current flows to the lamp. Figure 7B shows the same circuit as a schematic.

Power sources wired in parallel should each have the same voltage output.

With properly wired parallel power, the voltage output stays the same as either of the individual sources. Each source provides part of the current load. If there are two power sources, each source supplies half of the current. If there are three sources, each supplies one-third of the current. The total amperage supplied is found by adding the amperage of each power source.

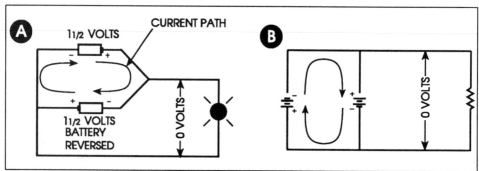

Fig. 7: Improper parallel voltage connection

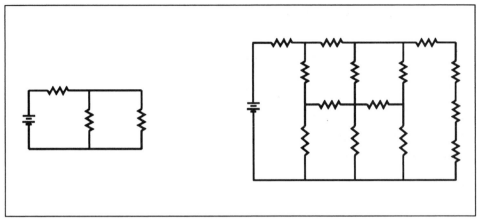

Fig. 8: Simple and complex series-parallel circuits

The advantage of parallel power comes when a single source cannot supply enough current. By adding additional power sources in parallel, the required current can be supplied. Parallel power is also used to extend the life of batteries. Batteries connected in parallel have less current drawn off them over time.

SERIES-PARALLEL CIRCUITS

A circuit may also be a **series-parallel circuit.** Series-parallel circuits combine elements of both types of circuit and can range from the simple to complex (Fig. 8).

REVIEW

If you can answer the following questions without referring to the text, you have learned the contents of this chapter. Try to answer every question **before** you check the answers in the back of the book.

1. There are three light bulbs in a room. When one light burns out, none of the lights work. Why?

2. Draw three light bulbs and connect them in a series circuit.

3. Draw three light bulbs and show how the wiring can be run so that each light operates independently.

4. What kind of a circuit did you draw for item 3 above?

5. If each of the three light bulbs in item 1 has a resistance of 2 ohms, what is the resistance of the circuit? (Disregard the resistance of the wiring.)

6. If the circuit in item 5 above was a parallel circuit, would the resistance still be 6 ohms?

7. In the drawing below, if each battery is 1½ volt, what is the voltage?

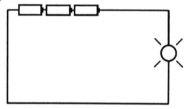

8. In the drawing below, how many volts are across the lamp?

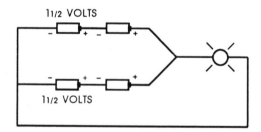

9. In the drawing below, how many volts are across the lamp?

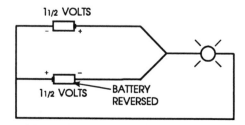

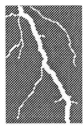

AC CIRCUITS

5

When you complete this chapter, you will be able to:

☐ Read and interpret a sine wave.

☐ Explain single-phase and 3-phase circuitry.

ALTERNATING CURRENT

Up to now we have talked mostly about DC (direct current) circuits. This is because DC circuits are the easiest to understand and the basic principles of DC are the same for AC. However, you will normally work with AC (alternating current) circuits. In addition to the principles you learned about DC circuits, there are new ones that apply to AC circuits. This chapter and Chapter 6 will explain these new principles.

Direct current is the flow of electrons in only one direction. When it flows in a circuit, direct current is at a constant value and stays at this value until it is turned off.

Alternating current (AC) is an alternating flow of electrons back and forth. The current rises and falls constantly, changing direction very rapidly. As you learned in Chapter 3, rotating a wire loop (an armature) in a magnetic field generates an electric current which changes direction.

An AC **cycle** occurs each time the current moves first in one direction and then in the other. In the United States, the standard current produced by utility companies is 60 cycle AC, which means that there are 60 cycles per second (or 120 changes per second). A cycle is called a **hertz (Hz)**. The term *60 Hz* means alternating current of 60 cycles per second.

In the United States, the typical home voltage is 110 or 120 volts. This is also the voltage that most hand tools run on. Higher voltage, such as 220 volts, is available for stoves and clothes dryers. Still higher voltage, such as 440 volts, is available for industrial use. Outside power lines leading into buildings can be 13,000 volts or more.

AC voltage can be stepped up and down with transformers. Chapter 10 will explain how transformers work. The ability to change the voltage easily is an advantage because it allows AC to be transported at high voltage and then stepped down to lower voltage at the point of use. This means smaller size primary conductors, and therefore lowers the cost of delivering power across country.

AC power can be delivered by two conductors (single-phase) or by three conductors with a neutral (3-phase).

☐ Single-phase power is common in residential build-ings.

☐ 3-phase power is common in large commercial and industrial buildings.

SINGLE-PHASE CIRCUITS

A 60 cycle **single-phase circuit** has only two conductors with voltage and current cycling 60 times a second. Single-phase voltage is represented by a single sine wave (Fig. 1). As you learned in Chapter 3, the sine wave curve is a diagram to represent one entire cycle of the AC voltage as the loop in the generator rotates:

☐ The horizontal line marked 0 represents zero po-tential (voltage).

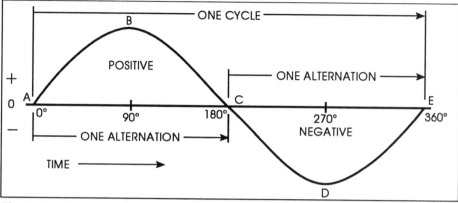

Fig. 1: A sine wave shows one complete cycle of AC current

☐ The first part of the sine curve, above the line, represents the first half of the cycle, when the voltage is positive.

☐ The second part of the sine curve, below the line, represents the second half of the cycle, when the voltage is negative.

At point A, the voltage is zero. Then it increases to peak positive at point B. At C, the voltage is again at zero. Past C the voltage reverses until it is at peak negative value at point D. It returns to zero at point E. The curve from A to E represents one cycle, called a **hertz (Hz)**. A current of 60 cycles per second is called 60 hertz (60 Hz).

The curve from A to E represents one revolution of the loop in the alternator. Point C represents 180° or half a revolution. Point E represents 360° or a complete revolution.

The power used in almost all residences is 60 cycle, single-phase AC. You will see this identified as 120 volt, 60 cycle (120V 60 Hz). Any small appliance that operates on 120 volts is single-phase equipment. Single-phase power can be used for almost all small heating, cooling, and refrigerating equipment. Most residences also have a 240 volt circuit used for such things as stoves and clothes dryers.

Single-phase power can be supplied by a 2-wire system or by a 3-wire system. The 2-wire system is found only on older buildings. This system supplies only 120 volts, and was used when there was no need for 240 volts. In the 2-wire system, one wire is hot and the other is neutral. The hot wire is the one that actually supplies the voltage.

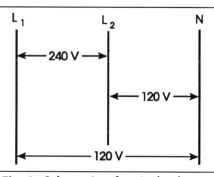

Fig. 2: Schematic of a single-phase 240 volt system

The most common single-phase voltage system today is the 240 volt system using three wires (Fig. 2). This system uses two hot wires plus one neutral wire (often called a **ground**). It can supply either 120 volts or 240 volts.

In Fig. 2, the hot wires are labeled L₁ and L₂ and the neutral wire is labeled N:

- ☐ Connecting both hot wires supplies 240 volts.

- ☐ Connecting either one of the hot wires to the neutral supplies 120 volts.

This single-phase 3-wire system is commonly connected to the main electrical panel in residences and light industrial buildings.

3-PHASE SYSTEMS

A 3-phase circuit has three currents alternating through it with equal time intervals between them. It is cheaper to transmit power long distances with a 3-phase system because the size of the wires is smaller since the current of each wire is less. It is also more economical to distribute power in large buildings with a 3-phase system.

Most commercial and industrial buildings use 3-phase AC power. One advantage of 3-phase power is that it can provide different voltages. Another advantage is lower cost. A third advantage is that motors using

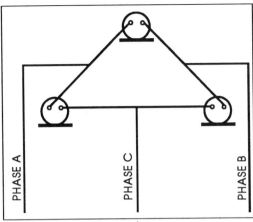

Fig. 3: Generating 3-phase power

3-phase power have better starting and running characteristics. In addition, larger motors are less costly and perform better if they are designed to operate on 3-phase power. Most large motors are 3-phase.

To create 3-phase power, three generators are wired together (Fig. 3). The three separate currents are produced at equal time intervals, 120° apart. There are three conductors (hot leads) plus a neutral wire. The three conductors all have the same voltage.

The sine wave in Fig. 4 shows how the three voltages in 3-phase power are related. Each curve represents one of the voltages of a single-phase current being transmitted. The three generators in Fig. 3 are adjusted so that when phase A is at peak, phase B is at 0; when phase B is at peak, phase C is at zero; etc.

The three hot leads (Phase A, B, and C in Fig. 3) and one neutral wire can be connected to make up a **3-phase hookup.** These four wires can be hooked up in different ways to provide different voltages, and to supply either single-phase or 3-phase power. This is covered in another book in this library series. For now, be aware that the connections in a 4-wire system can provide as high as 277 volts. If a circuit is incorrectly wired, voltage can be too high for the intended use. This can ruin equipment. If you work on 4-wire systems, be sure you know what you are doing and test wiring carefully.

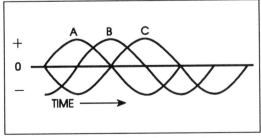

Fig. 4: Sine wave of 3-phase current

CIRCUIT PROTECTION

To prevent damage from a short circuit, some kind of circuit protection is needed for AC circuits.

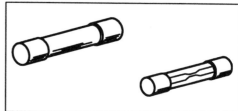

Fuses (Fig. 5) are designed to melt and break a circuit before the current gets high enough to damage the conductor.

Fig. 5: Fuses

Circuit breakers (Fig. 6) are switches that open when the amperage exceeds a safe amount. If a circuit breaker opens, it means there has been a problem in the circuit. Never close a circuit breaker switch until the problem that caused it to open has been located and repaired.

A **GFCI** (ground fault circuit interrupter) (Fig. 7) is an outlet that breaks the circuit if the amperage on each side of the energy user is not in balance beyond a set limit. It constantly monitors the electrical flow in the circuit. A GFCI is very fast and will break a circuit in a fraction of a second.

Fig. 6: Circuit breakers

Safety Note: Fuses and circuit breakers protect the circuit, equipment, and building from damage. However, they do not protect you from shock because they open the circuit after the electrical overload reaches a certain value. A GFCI does protect you because it opens the circuit immediately when a short occurs.

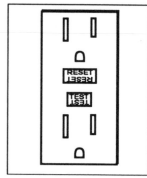

Fig. 7: A GFCI outlet

REVIEW

If you can answer the following questions without referring to the text, you have learned the contents of this chapter. Try to answer every question **before** you check the answers in the back of the book.

1. Add a letter from the sine wave drawing in each blank beside the list of items below.

   Peak positive voltage: _____

   One cycle: _____ to _____

   Peak negative voltage: _____

   Zero voltage between positive and negative voltage: _____

   180°: _____ to _____

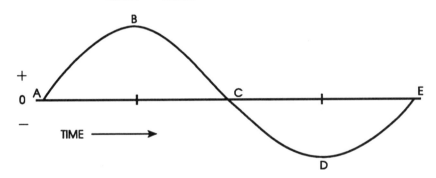

2. The power used in almost all houses in the United States is 120 volt, _____ cycle.

3. In the drawing below:
   A. Which lines would you connect to provide 240V?
   B: Which would you connect to provide 120V?

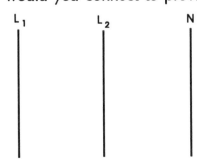

4. Give three advantages of three-phase power over single-phase.

5. What does the drawing below show?

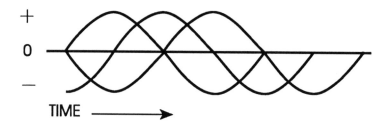

6

REACTANCE

When you complete this chapter, you will be able to:

☐ Define:

Inductive reactance

Capacitive reactance

Impedance

☐ Explain how inductive reactance affects an AC circuit.

☐ List the three factors that affect impedance.

RESISTANCE

Resistance (ohms) is the resistance to electrical flow in the conductor and in the loads. There is some resistance in even the best electric conductors, and there is resistance in any device connected to the circuit. A **resistive circuit** is a circuit in which the load (such as a heater, toaster, or incandescent lamp) is only a resistance. The resistance to electrical flow creates heat or light. Ohm's law states that **in a resistive circuit**, current flow (amperage) can be determined by dividing voltage by resistance (ohms):

$$\text{Amps} = \frac{\text{Volts}}{\text{Ohms}}$$

INDUCTIVE REACTANCE

Resistance affects the current draw of both DC and AC circuits. However, in AC circuits that have any device with a coil (such as an inductive motor, transformer, or fluorescent lamps), the amperage is also affected by a factor called **reactance**. The word **react** means to act against or oppose.

Chapter 3 explained how magnetism and electricity are related. When electric current flows through a conductor, a magnetic field is created around the conductor:

- If another conductor moves through the magnetic field, an electric current is induced in the second conductor.

- If a magnetic field moves past a conductor, an electric current is induced in the conductor.

In short, **induction** occurs when there is movement between the magnetic field and a conductor. This can be the result of the conductor moving through a magnetic field, or of the magnetic field moving past the conductor.

As alternating current moves through a conductor, the amperage and voltage continually rise and fall, as shown in a sine wave. As the voltage rises and falls, the magnetic field rises and falls. This has an important effect on a coil, which is a conductor looped around an iron core (See Chapter 3). Motors, transformers, solenoids, and other devices include a coil.

In a coil, the rising and falling of the magnetic field in one part of the coil moves the magnetic field past the conductor in another part of the coil. Figure 1 is a very simplified view of what happens. The rising and falling field created by portion A-B moves across portion C-D. If the current is rising, the magnetic field of A-B increases and induces a counterflow current from the induced voltage in portion C-D. The effect of the

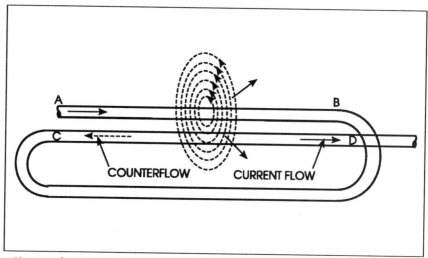

Fig. 1: The increasing magnetic field in one part of a coil induces current flow in another part of the coil

counterflow is to impede, or delay, the current in C-D. This effect is called **inductive reactance.**

☐ **Inductive reactance** opposes the current flow in an AC circuit:

When the voltage is **increasing,** the induced voltage tends to keep the current from increasing.

When the voltage is **decreasing,** the induced voltage tends to keep the current from decreasing.

When inductive reactance opposes changes in the flow of current in a circuit, it causes the amperage to be **out of phase** with voltage. The amperage lags behind voltage. Another way to say this is that voltage leads amperage.

Figure 2 shows the sine waves of voltage and amperage in an AC circuit with a coil. The sine wave for amperage lags 90° behind the sine wave for voltage. Amperage peaks after voltage, and it reaches zero after voltage does. The voltage and amperage are **out of phase.** This is the effect of inductive reactance.

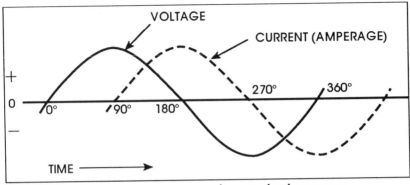

Fig. 2: Inductive reactance causes voltage to lead amperage

Inductive reactance is important because, when current and voltage are out of phase, more current is required to power a given electrical load. This means a higher cost for the required power. This will be explained in more detail in Chapter 8, Power Factor.

CAPACITIVE REACTANCE

A **capacitor** (formerly called a condenser) is a device that can store an electric charge and later release it. A capacitor can be used to oppose or resist changes in **voltage** in an AC circuit. This resistance to changes in voltage is **capacitive reactance** (also called **capacitance**). Chapter 7 explains how capacitors work.

Figure 3 shows the effect of capacitive reactance on the sine waves of voltage and amperage. Capacitive reactance is the opposite of inductive reactance—it causes amperage to lead voltage. Compare Figs. 2 and

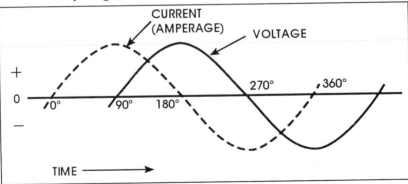

Fig. 3: Capacitive reactance causes amperage to lead voltage

3 and note how voltage and current are **out of phase** in both figures, but in opposite directions:

- ☐ **Inductive reactance** opposes changes in current flow (**amperage**).

- ☐ **Capacitive reactance** opposes changes in potential (**voltage**).

A capacitor installed in parallel with an inductive load can add capacitive reactance to a circuit to offset the effects of inductive reactance. This brings voltage and amperage more nearly into phase and reduces the amount of current necessary to power an inductive load. Chapter 8, Power Factor, explains why being out of phase is so important.

IMPEDANCE

In an AC circuit, the combined effect of resistance (ohms), inductive reactance, and capacitive reactance is called **impedance.** In an AC circuit:

$$\text{Impedence} = \frac{\text{Volts}}{\text{Amps}}$$

The Ohm's Law equation for resistance (ohms) in a purely resistive circuit is the same:

$$\text{Ohms} = \frac{\text{Volt}}{\text{Amps}}$$

This points out that impedance in an AC circuit has the same effect as resistance in a DC circuit.

The impedance in an AC circuit cannot be measured directly, because an ohmmeter cannot measure inductive reactance. It is not necessary for a technician to know the exact amount of impedance. You do need to know what affects impedance, and how impedance affects power factor.

REVIEW

If you can answer the following questions without referring to the text, you have learned the contents of this chapter. Try to answer every question **before** you check the answers in the back of the book.

1. What is the equation for Ohm's Law in a DC circuit?

2. Is reactance a kind of voltage, a kind of current, or a kind of resistance?

3. What condition is created when a conductor moves through a magnetic field or when a magnetic field moves past a conductor?

4. Name at least three items that include a coil.

5. What two conditions cause amperage to be out of phase with voltage?

6. What is the effect of adding a capacitor to a circuit?

7. What three factors make up impedance?

8. Can you measure impedance directly?

9. Is capacitive reactance likely to be desirable or not desirable in a circuit?

10. In the sine wave shown, does voltage lead amperage or amperage lead voltage?

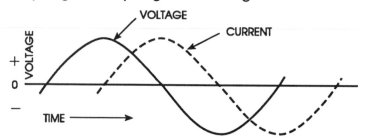

11. Does the sine wave above illustrate inductive reactance or capacitive reactance?

7

CAPACITORS AND CAPACITIVE REACTANCE

When you complete this chapter, you will be able to:

☐ Define capacitive reactance.

☐ Describe a capacitor and how it works.

CAPACITORS

You may encounter capacitors in HVAC equipment used for indoor environment systems. For example, they are used on capacitor-start motors. Chapter 6 described capacitive reactance and how it affects an AC circuit. This chapter explains how capacitors work.

Capacitors come in various shapes (Fig. 1). They are basically two plates of conducting material separated by an insulating material (Fig. 2). Figure 3 shows the symbol for a capacitor used on schematic diagrams.

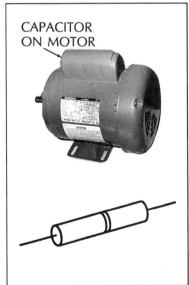

CAPACITOR ON MOTOR

Fig. 1: Capacitors

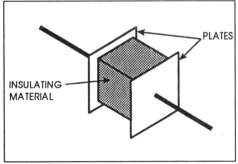

PLATES

INSULATING MATERIAL

Fig. 2: Basic construction of a capacitor

Operation

A capacitor is **charged** when one plate has a negative charge and the other plate has a positive charge. Since there is insulating material between the two plates, no current can flow from one plate to another. When a capacitor is charged, it holds an electrical potential (voltage) until it is discharged.

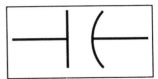

Fig. 3: Symbol for a capacitor

A capacitor is used in AC circuits. However, to see how it works, let's first look at it in a simple DC circuit. In Fig. 4, two plates are connected to the positive and negative terminals of a battery:

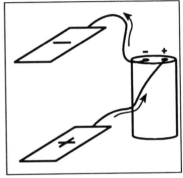

- ☐ Electrons flow from the negative battery terminal to the connected plate which becomes **negatively charged.**

Fig. 4: A charged capacitor

- ☐ The positive battery terminal attracts electrons from the plate connected to it. This plate becomes **positively charged.**

Because of the air or insulation between the two plates, no current will flow between the plates. Since this is a

---

Capacitors can remain charged for a considerable time after power is turned off. You can receive a shock from a charged capacitor even though the circuit is dead. Before working on a circuit, discharge the capacitor:

- ☐ *By grounding each terminal separately.*

- ☐ *By temporarily connecting the two terminals.*

With either method, you can be shocked. You must be insulated from the grounding device or the jumper wire.

Have an experienced technician show you how to discharge capacitors.

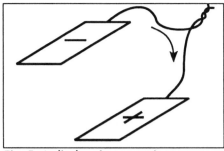

Fig. 5: A discharging capacitor

DC current, once the current reaches its full potential, no more current will flow in the circuit.

In Fig. 5 the battery is removed and the two wires are connected. This allows current to flow from the high potential (negative plate) to the low potential (positive plate). Current will flow until the two plates have an equal charge of electrons. The capacitor is then completely discharged.

Capacitors in an AC Circuit

In the DC circuit just described, as soon as the capacitor became charged, no current flowed in the circuit. In an AC circuit, the voltage is constantly alternating from positive to negative to positive, etc. As a result, the capacitor alternates between being charged and discharged.

Figure 6 shows what happens to the capacitor in one AC cycle:

❒ **A. First quarter (0° to 90°):** The applied voltage starts at zero at the start of a cycle and rises to

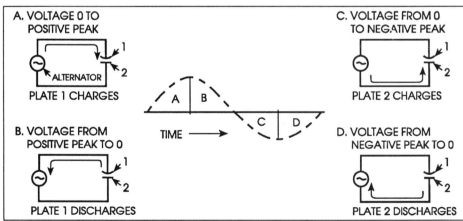

Fig. 6: The process of capacitive reactance

positive peak voltage. As the voltage rises, capacitor plate 1 is charged.

☐ **B. Second quarter (90° to 180°):** The applied voltage drops from positive peak to zero. The capacitor charge is greater than the applied voltage and capacitor plate 1 discharges. Note that the discharge is in the opposite direction from the charging cycle.

☐ **C. Third quarter (180° to 270°):** The applied voltage reverses to negative and goes from zero to negative peak voltage. Since the applied voltage is greater than the stored voltage in the discharged capacitor, the capacitor again charges. Note however that since the polarity of the applied voltage has changed, capacitor plate 2 charges. Note that the capacitor is charging in the same direction as when it was discharging.

☐ **D. Fourth quarter (270° to 360°):** The applied voltage goes from negative peak to zero. Since the capacitor charge exceeds the applied voltage, the capacitor again discharges. Note that it changes direction from the previous charging cycle.

Counter-voltage

In an AC circuit, the charge and discharge of the capacitor is called **counter-voltage** because its direction is opposite to the applied voltage. The circuit voltage and the applied voltage are 180° out of phase (Fig. 7). Since the capacitor voltage is in the opposite direction from the applied voltage, it tries to produce current flow in the

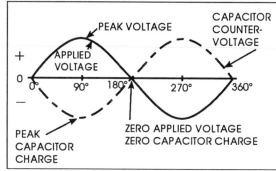

Fig. 7: Capacitor counter-voltage is 180° out of phase with applied voltage

opposite direction from the circuit current flow. This impedes the circuit current.

CAPACITIVE REACTANCE

In an AC circuit with a purely inductive load, the effect of the circuit voltage and the capacitor counter-voltage is that the current leads the voltage by 90°. In Fig. 8, at 90° the circuit current is at its peak but the circuit voltage is at 0.

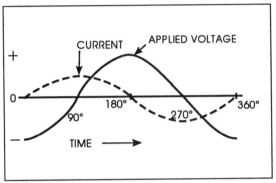

Fig. 8: Because of counter-voltage, the current leads the applied voltage by 90°

This process is **capacitive reactance** (also called **capacitance**). It has the opposite effect from inductive reactance. Capacitive reactance causes current (amperage) to lead voltage.

Capacitive reactance is important because it can be added to a circuit to offset inductive reactance, bringing voltage and amperage into phase. As a result, less current is needed to produce the required power.

Remember that **impedance** is the total of the resistance and inductive reactance in a circuit. Since capacitive reactance can offset inductive reactance, it affects the impedance of a circuit.

In Chapter 8 you will learn about power factor and how it affects the actual power being used in a system. Both inductive reactance and capacitive reactance directly affect power factor.

REVIEW

If you can answer the following questions without referring to the text, you have learned the contents of this chapter. Try to answer every question **before** you check the answers in the back of the book.

1. Draw the symbol for a capacitor.

2. The drawing below shows the sine wave of an AC applied voltage. Draw in the capacitor counter-voltage.

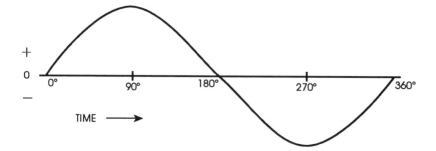

3. The drawing below shows the voltage of an alternating current in a circuit with a purely inductive load. Draw in the sine curve for the current with a capacitor in the circuit.

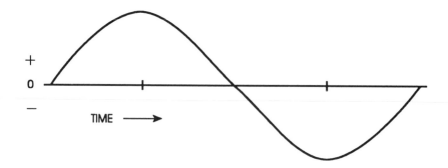

4. Does capacitive reactance cause the current to lead or lag the voltage?

5. Does inductive reactance cause the current to lead or lag the voltage?

6. The power to a capacitor-type motor is off. Is it possible to receive a shock when working on this motor?

7. You receive a shock from a circuit that you know is dead. How is this possible?

8  *POWER FACTOR*

When you complete this chapter, you will be able to:

- ☐ Explain the difference between real power and apparent power.

- ☐ Calculate apparent power.

- ☐ Calculate real power.

- ☐ Calculate power factor.

- ☐ Explain two ways in which poor power factor increases energy costs.

POWER

Power is the ability to do work. In electricity, power is expressed in watts. (For practical purposes, watts are usually converted to kilowatts. A kilowatt equals 1000 watts.) Power in a DC circuit is the product of volts multiplied by amps:

Power = Volts x Amps

For example, if a DC electrical circuit is measured at 12 volts and 20 amps, the power can be calculated by using the equation:

Power = Volts x Amps

Power = 12V x 20 A

Power = 240 W (watts)

Power = 0.24 KW (kilowatts)

APPARENT POWER

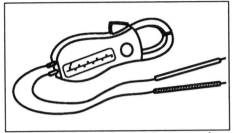

Fig. 1: A volt-ammeter measures volts and amps

The value of the current in an AC circuit is continually rising and falling. Therefore a volt-ammeter (Fig. 1) used to measure a circuit indicates the **average** value for the volts and amps. These readings are called the **effective current** and the **effective voltage.** The effective value is 0.707 times the peak value.

Apparent power is the power indicated by these readings on the volt-ammeter. When you measure the volts and amps to calculate the power, you are determining **apparent power.**

In a circuit that has a reading of 240 volts and 20 amps, the apparent power is 4.8 KW.

Apparent power = Volts x Amps

Apparent power = 240V x 20 A

Apparent power = 4800 Watts

Apparent power = 4.8 KW

PROBLEMS

1. What is the apparent power in kilowatts in a measured 120 volt, 20 amp AC circuit?

2. What is the apparent power in kilowatts in a measured 240 volt, 30 amp AC circuit?

(Answers are at the end of this chapter.)

REAL POWER

Real power is the actual power available for useful work.

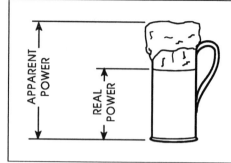

A glass of beer with a head of foam (Fig. 2) may appear to be full. But the real amount of beer may be less than a full glassful. Apparent power is like the beer with the head—it appears to be full. Real power is like the actual beer beneath the foam. It may be less than it appears to be.

Fig. 2: Apparent power is what appears to be. Real power is what actually is

Real power is volts times amps **at the same instant.** If the volts and amps are **in phase** in an AC circuit (Fig. 3), both the amps and the volts peak at the same time during each cycle. The apparent power and the real power are equal. However, in most AC electrical circuits—because of inductive reactance or capacitive reactance—the amperage cycle either lags or leads the voltage cycle:

☐ In circuits with a coil (such as induction motors, solenoids, and transformers), **inductive reactance** causes amperage to lag voltage (Fig. 4). This means that amperage reaches peak **after** voltage reaches peak.

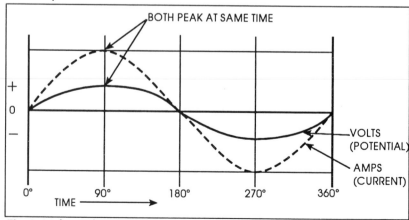

Fig. 3: Volts and amps in phase

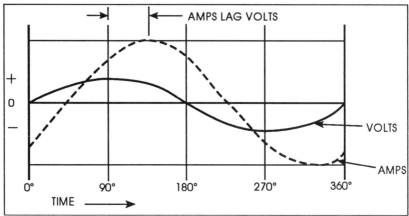

Fig. 4: **Inductive reactance** causes amperage to lag behind voltage

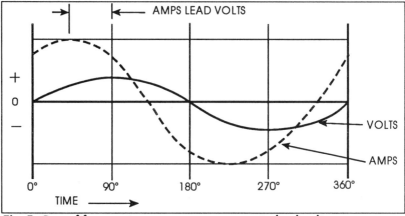

Fig. 5: **Capacitive reactance** causes amperage to lead voltage

☐ In circuits with capacitors, **capacitive reactance** causes amperage to lead voltage (Fig. 5). This means that amperage reaches peak **before** voltage reaches peak.

With either inductive reactance or capacitive reactance, the volts and amps are **out of phase.** If the volts and amps are out of phase, they do not peak at the same instant. When this happens, less than the apparent

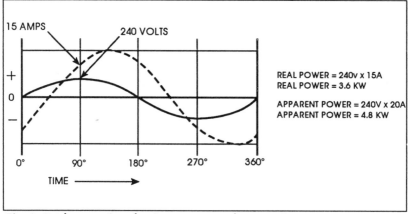

Fig. 6: Real power is volts times amps at the same instant

power is being delivered. **The apparent power and the real power are not the same.**

Apparant power is effective volts times effective amps, as measured by a volt-ammeter. If a volt-ammeter is used on the circuit shown in Fig. 6, the voltage measures 240 volts and the amperage measures 20 amps. The apparent power is 4.8 KW. (The volt-ammeter is often considered as measuring peak although it actually measures an average that is less than peak.)

Real power is amps times volts **at the same instant.** In Fig. 6, suppose that at 90° the peak voltage is 240V and the amperage at the same instant is 15A:

Real power = 240 volts x 15 amps

Real power = 3600 watts

Real power = 3.6 KW

POWER FACTOR

Power factor is simply the ratio of real power to apparent power:

$$\text{Power factor} = \frac{\text{Real power}}{\text{Apparent power}}$$

For example, in the circuit in Fig. 6, apparent power is 4.8 KW (240V x 20A) and real power is 3.6 KW (240V x 15A). These figures determine the power factor (Fig 7):

$$\text{Power factor} = \frac{\text{Real power}}{\text{Apparent power}}$$

$$\text{Power factor} = \frac{3.6}{4.8}$$

$$\text{Power factor} = 0.75 \ (75\%)$$

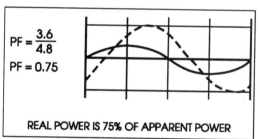

PF = $\frac{3.6}{4.8}$

PF = 0.75

REAL POWER IS 75% OF APPARENT POWER

*Fig. 7: If power factor is **less** than one, some power is not being used*

If power factor is 1.0 (100%), the volts and amps are in phase (Fig. 3) and maximum power is available. If the power factor is less than 1, some power is not being used.

If the power factor is known, it can be used to find real power:

Real power = Apparent power x Power factor

For example, for the circuit in Fig. 6, if the power factor (0.75) and apparent power (4.8 KW) are known, real power can be calculated:

Real power = Apparent power x Power factor

Real power = 4.8 KW x 0.75

Real power = 3.6 KW

PROBLEMS

3. In a 240 volt, 20 amp AC circuit that has a power factor of 0.90, what is the apparent power?

4. In problem 3, what is the real power?

DETERMINING POWER FACTOR

You can measure power factor directly by using a **power factor meter** (Fig. 8). This is the simplest way to determine power factor, but the power factor meter may not always be available.

Fig. 8: Determine power factor with a power factor meter

Power factor can also be calculated if real power is known. Measure real power with a **wattmeter**. Measure apparent power with a **volt-ammeter**. Then you can calculate power factor:

$$\text{Power factor} = \frac{\text{Real power}}{\text{Apparent power}}$$

PROBLEMS

5. In a measured 240 volt, 30 amp circuit, the real power is 6.84 KW. What is the power factor (to two decimal places)?

6. A wattmeter gives a reading of 4.6 kilowatts for the real power in a 230 volt system with a measured current of 28 amps. What is the power factor (to two decimal places)?

IMPORTANCE OF POWER FACTOR

A poor power factor costs money. A utility company often charges a **higher rate** for a building with a power factor below a set limit (such as 0.85). This is because generating equipment must be larger when many customers have an apparent power that exceeds the real power. When demand for electricity rises, the utility has to provide larger generating plants, transformers, and wiring. This is very expensive, so they want to encourage customers to avoid wasting energy. Therefore, most utility companies have a power factor meter on commercial and industrial buildings.

Two buildings doing the same kind of work may be identical except that one has a power factor of 0.95 and the other has a power factor of 0.69. The building with the 0.69 power factor may be charged a higher rate for that electricity.

In addition, the building with a poor power factor has greater costs. Larger transformers are required. The wiring may be at maximum current carrying capacity, so additional loads cannot be added unless more transformers and wiring are added. Because of the high current draw, the conductors are likely to suffer excessive line loss. This is an additional waste of energy.

IMPROVING POWER FACTOR

The power factor in a building can be improved by retrofitting the electrical system. A common retrofit measure is to replace old over-sized motors with properly sized, high efficiency motors that have a better power factor rating.

Another retrofit measure is to add capacitors to equipment to reduce the effect of inductive reactance.

Inductive reactance causes the amperage to lag the voltage. Adding capacitors offsets the effect of the inductive reactance and brings the amperage and voltage closer to being in phase.

REVIEW

If you can answer the following questions without referring to the text, you have learned the contents of this chapter. Try to answer every question **before** you check the answers in the back of the book.

1. Power is the ability to do _____.

2. One KW equals _____ _____.

3. Power = _____ x _____ .

4. A circuit is measured with a volt-ammeter as having 120 volts and 30 amps. How many KW are in the circuit?

5. In item 4 is the KW real power or apparent power?

6. The actual power available to do work is the _____ power.

7. Real power and apparent power are the same if the volts and the amps are in _____.

8. Power factor is _____ power divided by _____ power.

9. A circuit is measured at 240 volts and 40 amps. However the power factor in the circuit is 0.80.

   A. What is the real power?

   B. What is the apparent power?

10. A single-phase circuit is measured by a volt-ammeter as 240 volts and 45 amps. The same circuit is measured by a wattmeter as 7200 watts. What is the power factor for the circuit (to 2 decimal places)?

**ANSWERS TO
PROBLEMS**
 1. 2.4 KW
 2. 7.2 KW
 3. 4.8 KW
 4. 4.32 KW
 5. 0.95
 6. 0.71

9 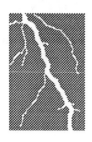 ELECTRICAL WORK

When you complete this chapter, you will be able to:

☐ Calculate electrical power and work.

☐ Convert between electrical and mechanical work units.

POWER AND WORK

The purpose of an electrical circuit is to provide electrical **power** to do **work** (energy). To perform useful work, electrical energy is converted into other kinds of energy such as:

☐ Light energy (lighting for buildings)

☐ Heat energy (resistance heaters)

☐ Mechanical energy (electric motors, solenoids, etc.)

You can calculate electrical power and electrical work (energy). You can also calculate the mechanical work that can be done by electrical power.

It is important to understand the difference between power and work.

☐ **Power** (demand) is the amount of energy available at any given moment. It is a measure of the **rate** of work that can be done.

☐ **Work** (energy) is the power used over a given period of time to perform a useful task.

Electrical **power** is measured in **watts** (W). For practical purposes, watts are usually converted to kilowatts by dividing by 1000 (moving the decimal point 3 places to the left). The power demands of a single-phase AC circuit can be determined with a simple equation:

Power = Volts x Amps x Power factor

For example, you can determine the power of a 120V single-phase circuit (with a power factor of 1) having 2 heaters—one using 10 amps and one using 15 amps:

Power = Volts x Amps x Power factor

Power = 120V x (10A + 15A) x 1.0

Power = 3,000 Watts

Power = 3 KW

This circuit requires 3 kilowatts of power.

For a 3-phase circuit, the equation for power is:

Power = Volts x Amps x 1.732 x Power factor

Therefore, if the circuit just described were 3-phase, the power would be this:

Power = 120V x (10A + 15A) x 1.732 x 1

Power = 5196 Watts

Power = 5.196 KW

Electrical **work** is measured in **kilowatt hours** (KWH), the number of kilowatts used in one hour (KW x Hours).

When you know that the power for this circuit with two heaters is 3 kilowatts, and you know that these heaters were on for 6 hours, you can determine how much work was performed, measured in kilowatt hours:

Work = KW x Hours

Work = 3 KW x 6 Hours

Work = 18 KWH

82

This circuit demand (power) is 3 KW. It performs 18 KWH of work (energy).

PROBLEMS

1. In a 220V single-phase circuit, a resistance heater is rated at 45 amps. How many watts is this?

2. How many kilowatts is this?

3. If this heater operates an average of 9 hours a day, how many kilowatt hours does the utility company charge for, over a thirty-day period?

(Answers are at the end of this chapter.)

MECHANICAL POWER AND WORK

When electrical power is used to run a motor, the motor produces **mechanical power**. The mechanical power may be used to drill, cut, run air conditioning equipment, or perform hundreds of other jobs.

Mechanical power is measured in **horsepower (HP)**. One horsepower is equal to 746 watts (for a 100% efficient motor). Watts can be converted to horsepower, or horsepower can be converted to watts:

Watts = Horsepower x 746

$$\text{Horsepower} = \frac{\text{Watts}}{746}$$

For example, you can calculate how many kilowatts are required by a fully loaded, 100% efficient 5 HP motor:

Watts = Horsepower x 746

Watts = 5 HP x 746

Watts = 3730

KW = 3.73

If you know that the motor runs for 8 hours a day, you

can calculate how many kilowatt hours are used in a day to do the mechanical work:

KWH = KW x Hours

KWH = 3.73 KW x 8 hours

KWH = 29.84

You may use these calculations to determine if a motor is overloaded or underloaded. For example, if an air handling system is not producing the required CFM, you may want to speed up the fan motor. However, if it is adjusted so that it is running above the rated horsepower, the motor may soon burn out. You will need to know how much actual horsepower (brake horsepower) the motor is using. **Brake horsepower (BHP)** is the load that is imposed on a motor by an energy user (such as a fan, pump, etc.). You can calculate BHP by taking a reading with an ammeter and converting the reading to horsepower. You also need to know the power factor (PF) and the rated efficiency of the motor (the term **Eff** and the rating is sometines stamped on the motor nameplate).

For a single-phase motor, use the following equation:

$$BHP = \frac{\text{Volts x Amps x PF x Eff}}{746}$$

For a 3-phase motor, use the following equation:

$$BHP = \frac{\text{Volts x Amps x 1.732 x PF x Eff}}{746}$$

For example, a 3-phase 240 volt fan motor is rated at 5 HP. You want to make sure that the motor does not run at more than 5 HP, so you use an ammeter to determine the load. The reading on the ammeter when the motor is operating at full load is 9.6 amps. The power factor is 88% and the Eff rating on the motor nameplate is 90%. Apply the equation:

$$BHP = \frac{240V \text{ x } 9.6A \text{ x } 1.732 \text{ x } 0.88 \text{ x } 0.90}{746}$$

BHP = 4.24

This is less than the rated load of 5 HP.

Another way to determine an approximate BHP is to measure the amps and compare that reading to the FLA (full load amps) on the motor nameplate.

More information on the motor nameplate data is included in another book in this series.

PROBLEMS

4. You have a 10 HP motor driving a fan on a 3-phase circuit and you want to increase the RPM. The measured data is:

   Volts = 238

   Amps = 22

   Power factor = 87%

   Nameplate motor efficiency = 92%

   What is the load on the motor under the measured conditions?

5. A fan motor on a 220V 3-phase circuit draws 24.3 amps. The motor efficiency is 93% and the power factor is 86%. The motor is rated at 10 HP. What is the actual horsepower being used (to 2 decimal places)?

6. The fan in problem 5 runs 8 hours a day, 5 days a week. For 4 weeks, how many kilowatt hours will the utility charge for (to the nearest whole number)?

REVIEW

If you can answer the following questions without referring to the text, you have learned the contents of this chapter. Try to answer every question **before** you check the answers in the back of the book.

1. Electrical energy is converted into other forms of energy to perform work. Name three of these forms of energy.

2. Electrical energy applied to an electric motor produces _____ energy.

3. The energy available at any moment is _____.

4. The power used in a given amount of time is _____.

5. Power is usually measured in _____.

6. Electrical work is measured in ____ ____.

7. The abbreviation for kilowatt hours is ____.

8. In a 240 volt single-phase circuit, a heater draws 30 amps. The heater runs for three hours.

   A.   How much power is needed?

   B.   How much electrical work is performed?

9. A 5 HP motor is running on a 240 volt 3-phase circuit that is drawing 9.6 amps. The power factor is 88% and the motor nameplate efficiency is 90%. What brake horsepower is the motor producing?

10. A 5 HP motor on a 240 volt, 3-phase circuit is drawing 2.7 KW. Motor efficiency is 81% and power factor is 91%. Can the fan belts be changed to speed up the fan without overloading the motor? Explain why or why not. Show calculations to prove your answer.

ANSWERS
TO PROBLEMS
1. 9,900 W
2. 9.9 KW
3. 2673 KWH
4. 9.73 BHP
5. 9.93 BHP
6. 1588 or 1589
   (depending on whether you round off the BHP)

10 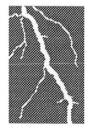 *TRANSFORMERS*

When you complete this chapter, you will be able to:

☐ Explain the operating principles of transformers.

☐ Describe at least three types of transformers.

☐ Identify transformers on schematic diagrams.

TRANSFORMERS

A **transformer** is an inductive device which isolates the entering circuit from the leaving circuit. It may either step down or step up the leaving voltage. Transformers can work only with alternating current.

Utility companies distribute electricity over power lines at extremely high voltages because it requires smaller conductors. The high voltage needs to be reduced to lower voltage by a transformer before it can be brought into buildings and used safely.

Sometimes the line voltage available in the building needs to be reduced even further by a transformer for a particular piece of equipment. On the other hand, voltage sometimes has to be increased by a transformer for a particular use. In certain situations, voltage from one circuit simply needs to be isolated from antoher circuit.

Transformers range in size from huge units with outputs of thousands of kilowatts to tiny transformers in electronic gear with outputs of a fraction of a milliwatt. Controls for indoor environment equipment often require transformers. For example, a transformer in a residential furnace may step the electrical current down from 120 volts to 24 volts.

HOW A TRANSFORMER WORKS

Chapter 3 explained **induction**. A magnetic field moving across a conductor induces an electric current in the conductor. This is the basic principle of the transformer.

Figure 1 is a schematic drawing of a transformer. The part of the transformer receiving electric current is called the **input** or **primary**. The circuit in which a current is induced is the **output** or **secondary**.

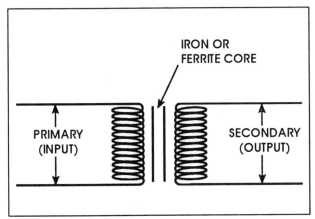

Fig. 1: Transformer schematic

A transformer has two insulated windings on an iron core. The winding of the primary, which is receiving power, creates a magnetic field. The coil is receiving alternating current, so each time the magnetic field rises and falls, it moves across the winding of the secondary. The moving magnetic field induces a voltage in the secondary.

The output voltage of a transformer is determined by the ratio of the number of turns of wire on the primary winding compared to the number of turns on the secondary winding. If the secondary has fewer turns than the primary, the secondary voltage will be less than the primary voltage.

Most transformers have cores made of iron or ferrite with primary and secondary windings on two sides of the core (Fig. 2). These cores help the magnetic field

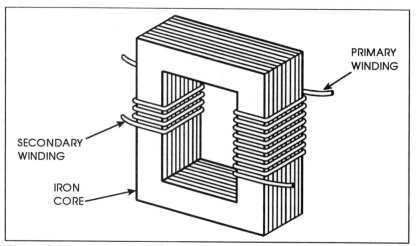

Fig. 2: One common type of transformer

work more effectively because they are good magnetic materials. The cores are laminated, and the thin metal plates are insulated from one another to reduce losses from induction.

Transformers come in many sizes and shapes in order to suit a wide variety of uses.

Transformers for high power voltage are enclosed in a shell to prevent their magnetic fields from dissipating and becoming less effective.

TYPES OF TRANSFORMERS

Step-down transformers convert a higher voltage to a lower voltage. A step-down transformer (Fig. 3) has more windings in the primary coil and fewer windings in the secondary coil.

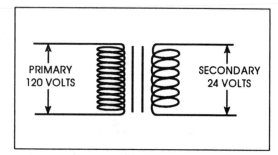

Fig. 3: Schematic diagram of a step-down transformer

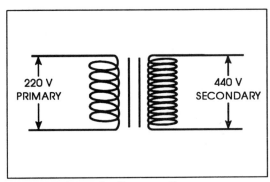

Fig. 4: Schematic diagram of a step-up transformer

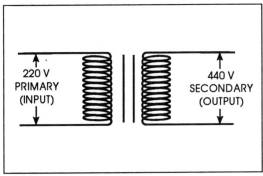

Fig. 5: Schematic diagram of a coupling transformer

The high voltage from power lines must be transformed to a lower voltage that can be used safely in a building. Within the building, a piece of equipment may use another step-down transformer to reduce building voltage to a still lower level. HVAC controls often use 24 volts, so a step-down transformer is used to reduce 120 volts to 24 volts.

Step-up transformers (Fig. 4) increase the voltage of the power being transferred. They have fewer windings in the primary coil and more windings in the secondary coil. Some pieces of equipment require step-up transformers. The ballast in a fluorescent lighting fixture is really a step-up transformer.

Isolating transformers (Fig. 5) transfer power from one circuit to another without changing voltage. An isolating coupling transformer can be used to separate electrical systems such as the system for a hospital intensive care unit and HVAC control circuits. An isolating transformer has the same number of windings in the primary and the secondary coils.

A **buck-and-boost transformer** can be wired to buck (decrease) or boost (increase) the voltage if it is a little too high or too low for the equipment.

Figure 6 is a schematics that shows transformers in a typical arrangement for an industrial building:

A. A step-down transformer at the service entrance to the building converts the high-voltage 3-phase power distributed by the utility company to lower voltages.

B. One line from the secondary is wired to produce a 480V line that serves the motors.

C. Another connection with the neutral wire produces a 277V circuit for the fluorescent lighting.

D. A step-down transformer is used to produce 120V lines for lighting and convenience outlets.

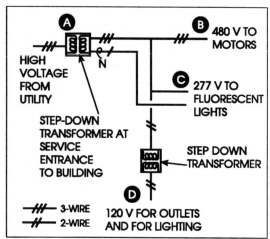

Fig. 6: Typical transformers for an industrial building

COOLING TRANSFORMERS

Transformers give off heat when they are operating. If a transformer becomes too hot, its insulation will burn off and the transformer will short out and have to be replaced.

Small transformers (for example, 120V primary—24V secondary) are air cooled. The surrounding air will carry off the heat. Some transformers also have fans that blow air over the case in order to carry off heat more quickly.

High voltage transformers are encased in a cover that contains a coolant oil. The coolant carries heat from the transformer to the case which gives off the heat to the surrounding air. The case is usually ribbed to expose as much surface to the air as possible. Outside transformers that serve a building should be located in cool, shaded areas if possible.

Older transformers sometimes contain the very dangerous coolant fluid PCB. If a thick and heavy fluid is oozing from a transformer case, it is probably PCB. Do not touch it! The transformer will have to be removed and disposed of in a special chemical waste dump. Newer transformers do not contain PCB.

CHOOSING TRANSFORMERS

Always choose the right transformer for a particular use. The voltage and current rating of a transformer should never be exceeded. This could destroy the windings. A label on the transformer (Fig. 7) will give the primary and secondary voltages. The primary and secondary connections will also be identified.

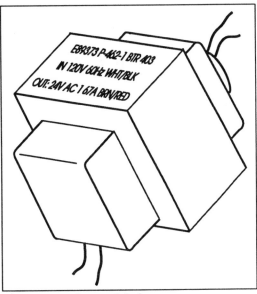

Fig. 7: Transformer label

CHECKING A TRANSFORMER

Use a voltmeter to check a transformer. With the primary supply circuit on, check the primary voltage. Next, check the secondary voltage. The secondary voltage should be within 10% of its rating. If there is no voltage on the secondary, either a fuse has blown or the transformer is defective.

REVIEW

If you can answer the following questions without referring to the text, you have learned the contents of this chapter. Try to answer every question **before** you check the answers in the back of the book.

1. Will a transformer operate on a DC circuit?

2. There are no moving parts on a transformer. How can a current be induced?

3. A step-down transformer has a set of terminals marked 120 volts and another set marked 24 volts. Which is the primary and which is the secondary?

4. Why do high voltage transformers contain a liquid?

5. Does the schematic drawing below show a step-up or a step-down transformer?

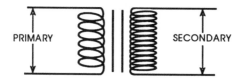

6. What is the basic electrical principle on which transformers operate?

REVIEW ANSWERS

Chapter 1

1. Answers can include the following: Damp skin, wet ground, metal-tipped shoes, 2-handed grip on a conductor, touching a grounded pipe

2. A. Hot wire

   B. Neutral

3. Insulators: Dry air, glass, rubber, plastic
   Conductors: Water, silver, aluminum, copper, human body

4. It can cause the circuit to get so hot that it burns through the insulation. Without insulation to keep it contained, electricity could cause shock or fire.

5. Battery, capacitor

6. It is an outlet designed to turn off immediately when a short occurs.

7. Unplug it and tag the plug.

8. Lock out and tag the main power source, the disconnect switch, or the control circuit.

9. The conductor could burn through the insulation and cause shock or fire, and a voltage drop could damage the equipment.

10. It is 911 in most areas. Find out if your area has a different emergency number.

Answers to the rest of the questions may vary. The following are good answers.

11. Turn off the circuit, if possible.
    Use dry wood to move the wire from the victim.
    Drag the victim away by using a rope, blanket, coat, belt, or other non-conductor.

12. The switch may be wired wrong, so there is still power in the circuit. You may get a shock from a capacitor that is storing electricity.

13. You didn't tag the electrical shut-off, and someone turned the power back on.

14. He may have been wet or standing on wet ground so that he made a good conductor. He may have had both hands on a grounded pipe so that the current went through his heart.

Chapter 2

1. 4.8 ohms

2. Decreased

3. 2.4 amps

4. 1.2 amps

5. AC—alternating currect
   DC—direct current

6. Answers can include such things as batteries, automobile circuits, electronic circuits

7. Resistive circuit

8. Reactive circuit

9. Resistive circuit

10. Fuse

11. A. Voltage

    B. Ohms

    C. Voltage

    D. Amperage

    E. Voltage

    F. Ohms

    G. Amperage

H. Ohms

I. Voltage

J. Ohms

12. Larger

13. Volts = Amps x Ohms

$$Amps = \frac{Volts}{Ohms}$$

$$Ohms = \frac{Volts}{Amps}$$

14. Resistive circuits

15. A. Fuse

B. Closed switch

C. Lamp

D. Motor

E. Open switch

F. Resistor

G. Double throw switch

H. Battery

Chapter 3

1. Answers can include the following:
Electric motors
Solenoids
Automatic switches
Transformers

2. Answers can include the following:
Iron
Nickel
Cobalt

Soft iron
Steel

3. Copper or aluminum

4. Induction

5. Electromagnet

6. Repel

7. Attract

8. Attract

9. Yes

10. B
    E
    C
    D

Chapter 4

1. They are on a series circuit.
2. Your art should be similar to Fig. 1 in the text.
3. Your art should be similar to Fig. 5 in the text.
4. A parallel circuit
5. 6 ohms
6. No
7. $4\frac{1}{2}$ volts
8. 3 volts
9. None

Chapter 5

1. B
   A to E
   D
   C

A to C (or C to E)
A to E

2. 60

3. A. L1 and L2

   B. L1 and N or L2 and N)

4. Can provide different voltages.
   Lower cost for power.
   Gives motors better starting and better running characteristics.

5. The sine wave of a 3-phase current

Chapter 6

1. Volts = Amps x Ohms
   or

   $$Amps = \frac{Volts}{Ohms}$$

2. A kind of resistance

3. Inductance

4. May include the following: motor, transformer, and solenoid

5. Inductive reactance

6. A capacitor stores voltage and releases it to resist changes in voltage.

7. Slow down

8. Not desirable

9. Desirable

10. Voltage leads amperage

11. Inductive reactance

Chapter 7

1.

2.

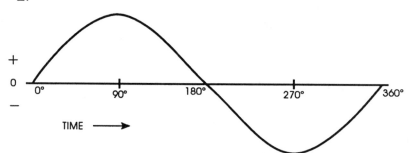

3.

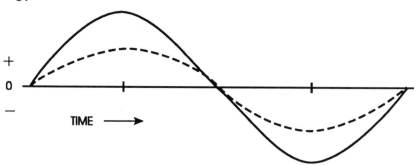

4. Lag

5. Lead

6. Until it is discharged

7. Yes

8. There is a capacitor in the circuit that has not been discharged.

Chapter 8

1. Work

2. 1000 Watts

3. Volts x Amps

4. 3.6 KW

5. Apparent power

6. Real

7. Phase

8. Real, apparent

9. A. 7.68 KW

   B. 9.6 KW

10. 0.67

Chapter 9

1. Light, heat, mechanical energy

2. Mechanical

3. Power

4. Work

5. Kilowatts

6. Kilowatt hours

7. KWH

8. A. 7.2 KW

   B. 21.6 KWH

9. 4.24 BHP

   $$BHP = \frac{\text{Volts x Amps x 1.732 x Power factor x Eff}}{746}$$

10. Yes, the fan can be speeded up because it is running well below its rated capacity of 5 HP.

    $$\text{Watts} = \text{Volts x Amps x 1.732 x Power factor}$$

    $$BHP = \frac{\text{Volts x Amps x 1.732 x Power factor x Eff}}{746}$$

$$BHP = \frac{Watts \times Eff}{746}$$

$$BHP = \frac{2700\ W \times 0.81}{746}$$

$$BHP = 2.93$$

Chapter 10

1. No

2. The AC current supplies the movement.

3. 120 volt primary and 24 volts secondary

4. To help cool them

5. Step-up

6. Induction

APPENDIX

EQUATIONS USED IN THIS BOOK

Ohm's Law: Volts = Amps x Ohms

$$\text{Amps} = \frac{\text{Volts}}{\text{Ohms}}$$

$$\text{Ohms} = \frac{\text{Volts}}{\text{Amps}}$$

Total resistance in a parallel circuit:

$$\text{Resistance} = \frac{1}{\left(\dfrac{1}{R_1}\right) + \left(\dfrac{1}{R_2}\right) + \left(\dfrac{1}{R_3}\right) + \left(\dfrac{1}{R_4}\right)}$$

R_1 through R_4 = Resistance of resistors in circuit

Impedance in an AC circuit:

$$\text{Impedance} = \frac{\text{Volts}}{\text{Amps}}$$

Power factor:

$$\text{Power factor} = \frac{\text{Real power}}{\text{Apparent power}}$$

Power in a DC circuit:

Power = Volts x Amps

Apparent power in an AC circuit:

Apparent power = Volts x Amps

Real power in an AC circuit:

Real power = Apparent power x Power factor

Real power in a single-phase AC circuit:

Real power = Volts x Amps x Power factor

Real power in a 3-phase AC circuit:

Real power = Volts x Amps x 1.732 x Power factor

Work (energy):

Work = KW x Hours

Converting watts and horsepower:

Watts = Horsepower x 746

$$\text{Horsepower} = \frac{\text{Watts}}{746}$$

Brake horsepower for a single-phase motor:

$$\text{BHP} = \frac{\text{Volts x Amps x Power factor x Eff}}{746}$$

Eff = Efficiency given on motor nameplate

Brake horsepower for a 3-phase motor:

$$\text{BHP} = \frac{\text{Volts x Amps x 1.732 x Power factor x Eff}}{746}$$

INDEX

LAMA Books also publishes:

LAMA BOOKS ORDER FORM

SHIP ORDER TO:

NAME_____ TITLE_____

FIRM_____

STREET ADDRESS_____

CITY/STATE/ZIP CODE_____

TELEPHONE (____)_____

MAKE CHECK PAYABLE TO: **LAMA** Books
Leo A. Meyer Associates
23850 Clawiter Road
Hayward CA 94545-1723
PHONE: 510•785•1091
FAX 510• 785•1099

DESCRIPTION	Number of Copies	Amount	Total
Please enroll me as a subscriber to the ***Indoor Environment Technician's Library*** and send me the latest book in the series, ***Airflow in Ducts*** (at a 20% discount). (I understand that future titles will be sent periodically on approval and I may return them if they do not fit my purposes.)		$14.00 ea.	
Airflow in Ducts (individual copy) *Supervisor's Guide*		$17.50 5.00	
Basics of Electricity (individual copy) *Supervisor's Guide*		$17.50 5.00	
Occupational Programs in California Public Community Colleges		$26.50	
Occupational Programs in the Western States		$27.50	
Catalog for ***The Reading Program Books A-G***		No charge	
Teach! Plain Talk about Teaching		$19.95	
		Subtotal	
		CA Sales tax (CA residents)	
		TOTAL	

PAYMENT:

☐ **CHECK ENCLOSED FOR TOTAL AMOUNT DUE**

☐ **PLEASE BILL ME**

☐ **PURCHASE ORDER ATTACHED**